THE
ELECTROPLATER'S
HANDBOOK

To Hazel, my daughter Sharon, and Ron

THE
ELECTROPLATER'S
HANDBOOK

C.W. AMMEN

TAB BOOKS

Blue Ridge Summit, PA

Other TAB Books by the Author

No. 1043   *The Complete Handbook of Sand Casting*
No. 1173   *The Metalcaster's Bible*
No. 1810   *Casting Brass*
No. 1910   *Casting Aluminum*

FIRST EDITION
SIXTH PRINTING

© 1986 by **TAB Books**.
TAB Books is a division of McGraw-Hill, Inc.

Library of Congress Cataloging-in-Publication Data

Ammen, C. W.
    The electroplater's handbook.

    Includes index.
    1. Electroplating.   I. Title.
TS670.A77   1986   671.7'32   86-1939
ISBN 0-8306-0410-3
ISBN 0-8306-0310-7 (pbk.)

TAB Books offers software for sale. For information and a catalog, please
contact TAB Software Department, Blue Ridge Summit, PA 17294-0850.

Contents

Introduction

The purpose of this book is to give you enough usable information whereby you can get into electroplating with a minimum amount of expenditure and absolutely no previous knowledge of the subject or of the chemistry involved. It can be that the information given in this book is all you need or desire. Then you are off and running doing your thing. Perhaps the information given in this book will simply serve as a starter for bigger and better things.

The study and practice of electroplating can become a lifetime pursuit. There is lots to be learned by further research and digging. New methods, procedures, formulas, and chemistry are ever changing in this field. Perhaps you might, through your research and experimentation, come up with some novel and important development in this field.

There are other books on electroplating. Some are simply too technical for the beginner or novice, but they are good references for a plating chemist. Some are so brief and simplified that they are useless for someone wanting to actually do some plating. They give only a general idea of what electroplating is about.

Whether you want to do some plating for your own amazement, as a hobby, or make a business of it, this book will get you rolling with good, simple equipment, advice, and workable formulas. There is advice on working with a small, tabletop operation in beakers or mason jars to a medium-sized commercial operation.

How far you go is up to you. You might even get interested

in electro chemistry, which is a fascinating field of study. Regardless of your goals, this volume will do the job. It is a real how-to-do-it, no-nonsense electroplating book.

Chapter 1

Principles of Electroplating

This is a hands-on, do-it-yourself book for the electroplater. Because electroplating is actually an electrical chemical proposition, the plater should understand basically what is going on and why.

METAL SALTS

Very simply the metal you wish to plate with must first be put into a solution in the form of its ions. Now an ion is a positively charged atom of the metal with which we wish to plate. Positive ions plus are called cations and negative minus ions are called anions. The principle is that ionic compounds consist of positive and negative charged atoms or groups of atoms. When these ionic compounds are dissolved or are in the molten state, and if you pass an electric current (dc), the cations will be attracted to the negative pole and the anions will be attracted to the positive pole. See Fig. 1-1. This is the basis of electroplating (electrolysis).

ELEMENT, SUBSTANCE, AND COMPOUND

An element is any substance made up of only one kind of an atom—and only one kind—such as hydrogen, oxygen, gold, iron, silver, or copper. A substance is any liquid, solid or gas made up of atoms.

A compound is any substance that is made up of two or more different kinds of atoms. Some elements (for example, hydrogen)

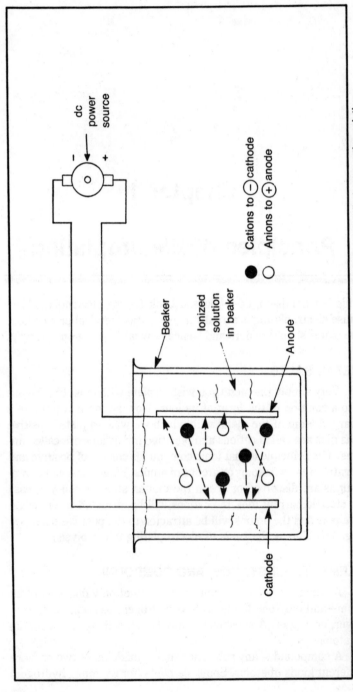

Fig. 1-1. Direction of travel of cations and anions in an ionized solution when dc potential is applied across the solution.

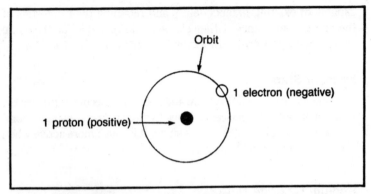

Fig. 1-2. Ring structure of one hydrogen atom.

usually consist of two atoms of hydrogen coupled together (designated as H_2 or two atoms of hydrogen). As they are both hydrogen atoms, you are still dealing with an element. Even though hydrogen is indicated by the symbol H it is usually in the form of two hydrogen atoms H_2. A hydrogen atom is illustrated in Fig. 1-2.

You have a nucleus containing one proton (plus) around which is circulating one electron (minus). This gives a kind of wobbly existence to the hydrogen atom so it usually couples itself up with another hydrogen friend to make a more stable situation.

If two hydrogen atoms get together they form a molecule of hydrogen. They do this by sharing electrons. See Fig. 1-3.

A Molecule

A molecule is defined as the smallest portion of a substance

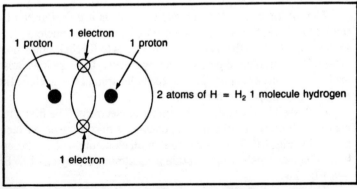

Fig. 1-3. Two hydrogen atoms coupled to make a molecule of hydrogen.

3

capable of existing independently and retaining the properties of the original substance. Other elements do this also for the same reason hydrogen does. An example is chlorine. See Fig. 1-4.

Nascent State

When alone as a single atom and not as a molecule or molecules, an atom is said to be nascent. Thus hydrogen (as H, a single atom) is called nascent hydrogen in this stage. It is much more active when set free in a chemical reaction.

Sodium Chloride NaCl

Let's look at the compound consisting of the metal sodium and the gas chlorine. Both are elements, and in combination produce the compound we call table salt: sodium chloride. The suffix *ide* after *chlor* simply indicates that this is a binary compound consisting of the two named elements. In this case it is sodium (a metal) and chlorine (a gas). Binary compounds are named by using the metal element first, followed by the nonmetal element, and followed by the suffix ide: copper chloride, silver chloride, gold chloride.

Now, let's look at the two separately. Sodium (Na), also called natrium, is a soft white metal that oxidizes very rapidly in oxygen. In water it decomposes with great violence (explosively) to form sodium hydroxide, NaOH.

Let's look at the sodium atom to see why it is so active. Metallic sodium is never found in the free state, but only as a component of a compound. See Fig. 1-5.

Sodium, Na, Atom

The orbits around the nucleus of an atom are designated by the letters KLMNOPQ; K is the orbit closest to the nucleus, L is second, etc. Now with all atoms the desire is to fill their outermost orbit with a complete 8-electron configuration. Let's look at these orbital electrons as shells. The more shells around the nucleus the tougher the atom is to break down.

Each shell holds a different number of electrons. The first shell nearest to the nucleus (the K shell) contains a maximum of two electrons. See Fig. 1-6. This holds true for all elements without exception. The next shell L can contain a maximum of 8 (from 1 to 8). See Fig. 1-7.

The third shell (M) can contain a maximum of 18 electrons.

4

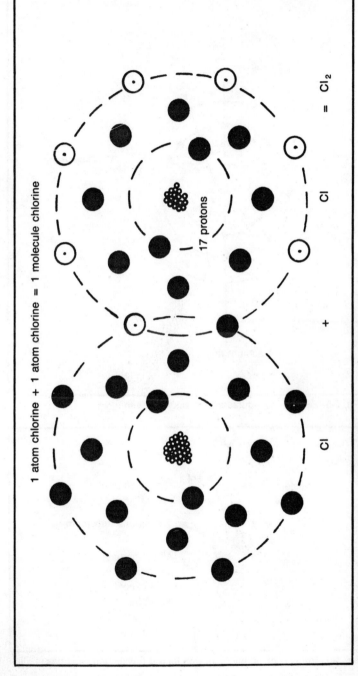

1 atom chlorine + 1 atom chlorine = 1 molecule chlorine

17 protons

Cl + Cl = Cl_2

Fig. 1-4. Two chlorine atoms share a pair of electrons and form a chlorine molecule Cl_2.

5

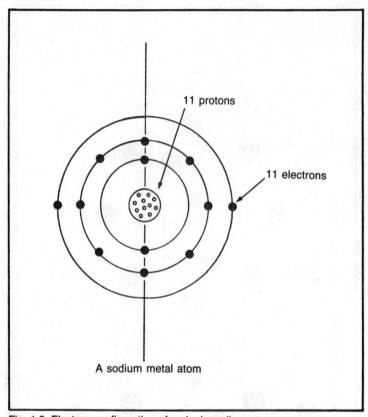

Fig. 1-5. Electron configuration of a single sodium atom.

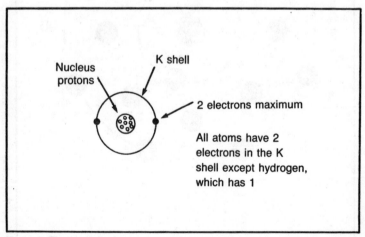

Fig. 1-6. The K shell of any atom with its two (maximum) electrons.

6

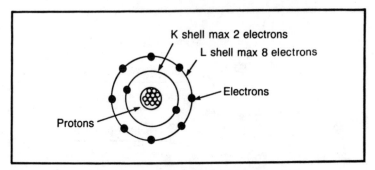

Fig. 1-7. The L shell of any atom with its eight (maximum) electrons.

See Fig. 1-8. The fourth shell (N) can contain a maximum of 32 electrons.

You might wonder where I am headed with this and why. We are concerned with plating and we must have a metal ion in solution in order to plate the metal of our choice onto the object. Therefore, we must be able to reduce the metal of our choice to a salt we can dissolve into a solution in order to get the desired positive ions into the solution free to swim around. By placing a negative charge on our object we wish to plate we can get these positive ions to go to the negatively charged item and neutralize themselves. In doing so the ions are reduced to the metal of the ions attaching this metal to the object we are plating. More on this later.

BACK TO SALT

The elements that have one, two, or three electrons in their outer shells are metals. Those with more than three electrons are nonmetals. The exception to this rule is elements such as carbon, silicon, germanium, that have four electrons in their outer shell.

These elements, especially carbon, are neither metals nor nonmetals. It is the outer shell that reacts. All atoms are trying to complete their outer shell with eight electrons. An atom with one, two, or three electrons in their outer shell is said to have a plus valence. That is they have one, two, or three electrons that they can donate or share with an atom or atoms that have seven, six, or five electrons in their outer shell and need these to complete their eight electrons. The acceptance of these electrons completes the donor atom (H_2O, water). You have one oxygen atom with an outer shell that is minus two electrons to complete itself. The hydrogen atom has one electron it can donate. It takes two

7

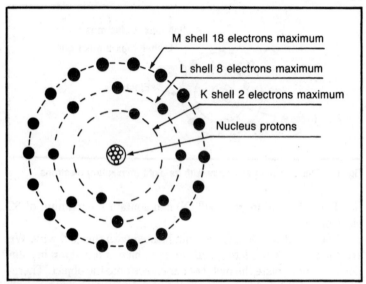

M shell 18 electrons maximum

L shell 8 electrons maximum

K shell 2 electrons maximum

Nucleus protons

Fig. 1-8. The K, L and M shells of an atom.

hydrogen atoms, each having a plus 1 valence, to fulfill the oxygen's outer shell, which is short 2 electrons having a minus two valence. See Fig. 1-9.

Let's look at salt sodium chloride. The sodium atom has two electrons in the K shell, eight electrons in the L shell and one electron in the M shell. Therefore, it has a plus one valence and the chlorine atom has two electrons in the K shell and 8 electrons in the L shell and 7 electrons in the M shell, which gives it a minus 1 valence. So the sodium needs to give up one electron to give it stability and the chlorine needs one electron to complete its outer shell's desire for 8 electrons, a perfect marriage. See Fig. 1-10.

Remember that the number of electrons an atom will gain or lose is its valence. In combining to form compounds, the atom will take the shortest route possible in any chemical reaction. If it has 6 empty spaces with two electrons, it will donate the two to the reaction. If it is short two spaces and has six electrons, it will not give up the six, but will accept two to accomplish the bond or reaction. Therefore, if you know the electronic arrangement of the elements you can easily deduce what will happen.

POSITIVE IONS AND NEGATIVE IONS

An ion is an atom that carries an electric charge, positive or

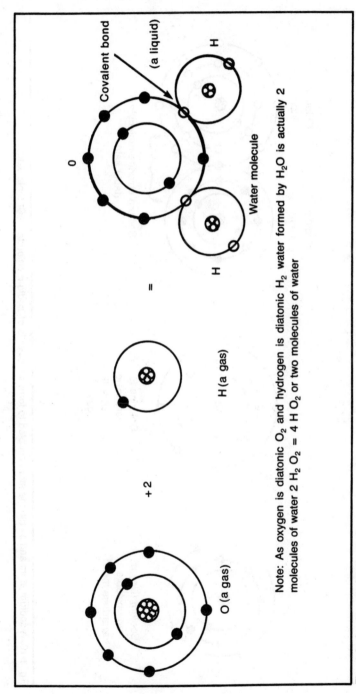

Note: As oxygen is diatonic O_2 and hydrogen is diatonic H_2 water formed by H_2O is actually 2 molecules of water $2 H_2 O_2 = 4 H O_2$ or two molecules of water

Fig. 1-9. A water molecule H_2O.

9

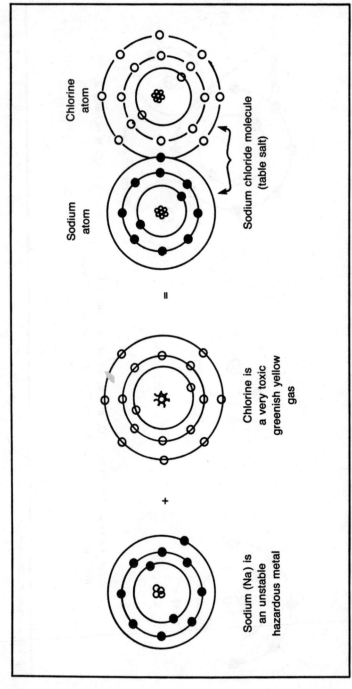

Fig. 1-10. A sodium atom and a chlorine atom coupled to form a molecule of sodium chloride NaCl table salt.

10

negative. Ions that are positive in their charge are called cations and ions which are negative in their charge are called anions. Let us see what would make an ion negative or positive.

Our salt (NaCl) has one atom of sodium coupled with one atom of chlorine. The salt NaCl doesn't resemble either sodium (a malleable white metal) nor does it resemble chlorine, which is a very toxic greenish yellow gas. Now let's look at an atom of sodium by itself and an atom of chlorine by itself. See Fig. 1-11.

Figure 1-11 shows a very basic illustration of a sodium atom. In the center is the nucleus containing 11 positive electrical particles, called protons, around which orbit 11 negative particles distributed in three shells or orbits (L, M and N). It is now obvious that, if we have 11 positive particles and 11 negative particles, they cancel each other out giving you an "0" electrical charge (or value) for our one atom of sodium. Now when we donated the one lone electron in the N shell of our sodium atom to form up a bond with chlorine to make sodium chloride we upset the neutral or "0" electrical charge of our sodium atom. See Fig. 1-12.

So our sodium atom is robbed of one of its electrons (which is donated to the chlorine atom) and is now out of electrical bal-

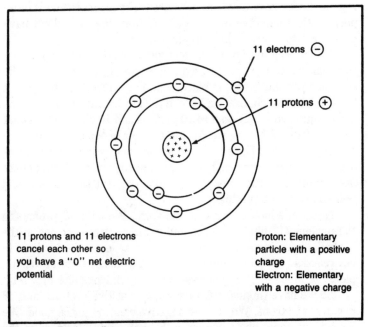

11 electrons ⊖

11 protons ⊕

11 protons and 11 electrons cancel each other so you have a "0" net electric potential

Proton: Elementary particle with a positive charge
Electron: Elementary with a negative charge

Fig. 1-11. Basic sodium atom.

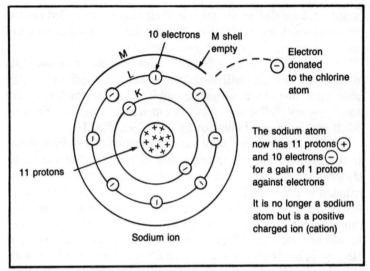

Labels within figure:

10 electrons

M shell empty

Electron donated to the chlorine atom

M

L

K

11 protons

The sodium atom now has 11 protons (+) and 10 electrons (−) for a gain of 1 proton against electrons

It is no longer a sodium atom but is a positive charged ion (cation)

Sodium ion

Fig. 1-12. Sodium atom with one electron donated to a chlorine atom now has a net positive potential of one extra proton.

ance. We now have 11 positive particles in the nucleus but only 10 negative particles, 2 in K shell and 8 in the L shell. The M shell is gone. So we have a condition where we have an ion that is more positive than negative by 1 positive proton. Now you don't have a sodium atom but a plus cation.

To get back to an atom of any type we have to get back a neutral charge ("0"). If we add an electron, we are back to a metallic sodium atom. Let's say, in place of adding an èlectron to bring it to "0" electrical charge, we instead took away one of the protons. This would even things out to 10 protons and 10 electrons. Would we have sodium? No, we would have an atom of neon. See Fig. 1-13.

Boy, this would be a real stopper because neon has a complete outer shell of 8 electrons. Therefore, it needs none nor will donate any. In other words, it is now a happy element that is inert and will combine with nothing.

Now, let's look at our chlorine atom. We have 17 protons in the nucleus (17 plus particles) and we have two electrons in the K shell, eight electrons in the L shell and seven in the M shell. In our reaction, we picked up one electron from the sodium to complete the M shell. This gives us an ion which looks like Fig. 1-14.

So we have (minus) chlorine ion, 17 positive protons, and 18 negative electrons. We are one negative electron to the good. We have 17 protons, two electrons in K shell, eight electrons in the

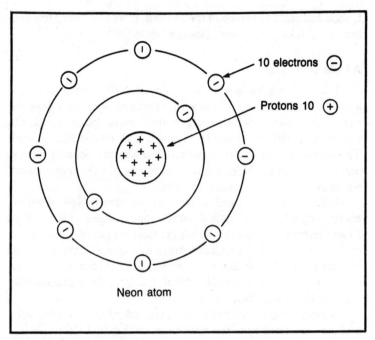

Fig. 1-13. Basic neon (gas) atom.

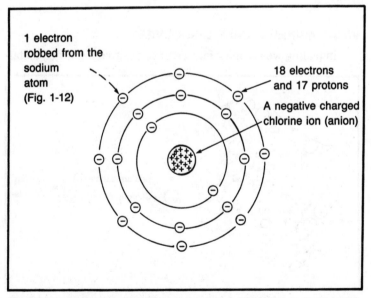

Fig. 1-14. A chlorine atom that has accepted one electron from a sodium atom to produce a chlorine ion (anion).

L shell and eight electrons in the M shell. If we took away one proton, we would have Argon (another inert gas).

ATOM OR ION?

From all this, looking at our sodium chloride (NaCl), we have a compound consisting of one atom of sodium and one atom chlorine. Now we know we cannot get one atom of sodium to stick to one atom of chlorine because they are both electrically neutral. There is no attraction between them. So what we actually have is one (minus) ion of chlorine attracted to one (plus) ion of sodium, which is called an electrovalent bond.

Like charges repel and unlike charges attract. Now, if we get enough of these (plus) ions and (minus) ions we have what is known as an electrovalent crystal. A salt crystal consists of a gang of sodium atoms in their ionic state hooked to a gang of chlorine atoms in their ionic state hooked together by electrical attraction differences. This is what you could call atomic glue. So a sodium chloride crystal would look like Fig. 1-15.

Now don't get confused with all this attention to atoms, salts, and ions. You will soon see what I am leading up to, the relationship to electroplating, and why you should understand what happens.

WHAT MAKES A SALT DISSOLVE?

In plating we are most interested in positively charged metal-

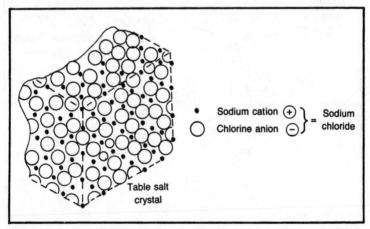

Fig. 1-15. Sodium chloride crystal consisting of chlorine anions (−) and sodium cations (+) in great numbers bound together by electrical attraction.

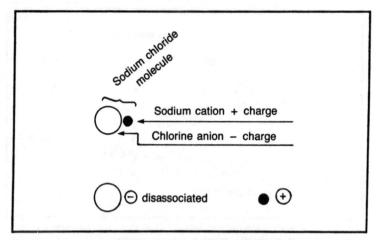

Fig. 1-16. Sodium chloride molecule together and disassociated.

lic ions. This is the heart of our plating process. For copper plating we need copper ions, for silver, silver ions, etc., but in order to get metallic ions we must first convert the metal into a salt of that metal. Copper sulfate, silver nitrate, etc., gives us metallic salt compounds consisting of (plus) and (minus) ions.

Now how do we disassociate the (plus and (minus) ions so that we can move the (PLUS) metallic ions over to the object we want to plate, and then reduce it back to a metal atom attached to the object? The process we are first interested in is freeing the bond between the (plus) and (minus) ions, separating them without changing their atomic structure. So with our salt (NaCl) we have one sodium ion and one chlorine ion. See Fig. 1-16.

The process is called hydrolysis and is the chemical decomposition of a substance by water. The water itself is also decomposed (Ab plus H_2O equals Na (OH) plus HCl or sodium chloride plus water equals sodium hydroxide plus hydrogen chloride). The (OH) consists of one hydrogen and one oxygen atom forming a part of a molecule of a compound. In inorganic compounds containing electrovalently bonded compounds, such as our NaCl, are hydrocyl groups that are alkalis.

Now in order to dissolve our salt (NaCl) disassociate the Na ions from the Cl ions to give them freedom. They must move around freely, independent from each other, so we can move them via an outside applied electric potential in the direction we choose. We must apply a stronger plus or minus from another source to pull them apart so to speak. Now remember these are not atoms but

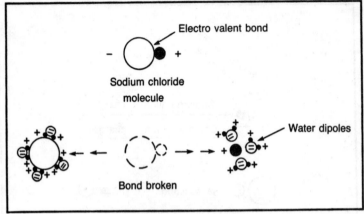

Fig. 1-17. Separating the sodium cation (+) from a chlorine anion (−) of a salt molecule by applying a stronger force externally.

ions: sodium ion and chlorine ion.

If two objects are held together by their electrical attraction and if we apply a stronger attraction from the opposite direction, they can be dislodged. See Fig. 1-17. How do we accomplish this disassociation? We simply add the salt to water where it dissolves and the Na ions (minus) and chlorine ions (plus) disassociated from each other and are free to swim about in the solution.

To understand why and how this happens we have to look at a water molecule H_2O. Oxygen has a minus two valence and hydrogen a plus one valence. So we get a hookup of two hydrogens and one oxygen in a configuration which looks like Fig. 1-18.

What we have here is a dipole defined as a molecule in which the centers of positive and negative charges are separated. See Fig. 1-19.

Fig. 1-18. Water molecule angle of bonding hydrogen atoms to oxygen atom.

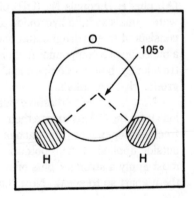

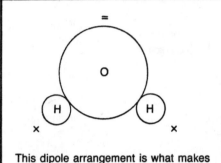

Fig. 1-19. Water molecule as a dipole.

This dipole arrangement is what makes water molecules a solvent for polar molecules such as sodium chloride, gold chloride, copper sulfate, etc.

Therefore, if we have a crystal of salt sodium chloride in water the water molecules (being dipoles) are going to pick the salt apart. The dipoles of H_2O do the trick. See Fig. 1-20.

We wind up with the sodium and chlorine ions separated and isolated from each other by the water molecules. See Fig. 1-21.

What are we talking about? The water dipoles immediately exert an attractive force on the ions forming the surface of the salt crystals. The negative oxygen end of several H_2O dipoles will exert its attractive force on a positive sodium ion. Likewise, the positive hydrogen ends of the H_2O dipoles will exert an attractive force on the negative chlorine ion. This is what weakens the bond

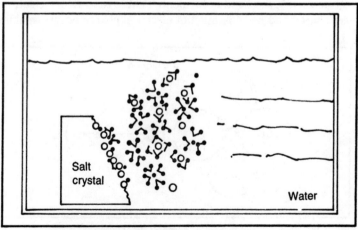

Fig. 1-20. Water dissolving salt (NaCl).

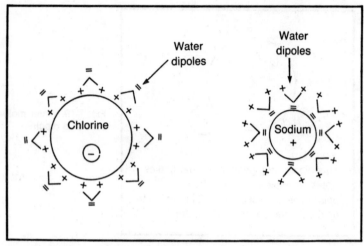

Fig. 1-21. The water dipoles surround both the sodium cation and the chlorine anion, keeping them from reforming into a salt NaCl.

between the Na ion and Cl ion and breaks them away from their crystalline pattern. Now, they are free to diffuse in the solution. This is what makes a salt dissolve in water. This process is reversible by simply evaporating the water. With the H_2O dipoles gone, the salt Na ions plus will group back with the Cl ions to form salt crystals.

Note. Not all molecules are dipolar. For example, the carbon tetrachloride (tetra is the prefix designation four, fourfold) molecule would look like Fig. 1-22. In some substances like carbon tetrachloride, the bond is covalent. That is the valence electrons are shared and no separation of electrical charge occurs, making

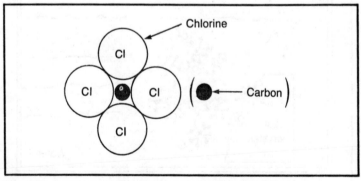

Fig. 1-22. Atomic arrangement of carbon tetrachloride.

a molecule with a symmetrical electrical field with cannot be acted on by H_2O dipoles to produce ions.

THE KEY TO ELECTROPLATING

Simply we have to get ions of the desired metal into a solution free to move about unattached and then apply an electrical potential to the solution so we can move them to where they will be converted back to a metallic atom.

If we were to soak a piece of copper in water, it is not going to put the copper into solution as ions. We must, in order to accomplish this, first convert the copper to a salt compound. If we digest copper metal in sulfuric acid and water and evaporate off the water (crystallization), we wind up with a copper sulfate salt that consists of $CuSO_4$.$5H_2O$. These blue crystals are called a copper hydrate (a crystallized substance that contains water of hydration).

$CuSO_4$.$5H_2O$ simply means five molecules of water are combined with one molecule of copper sulfate. If we heated the $CuSO_4.5H_2O$ above the boiling point of the water molecules, they would vaporize and you would then have anhydrous $CuSO_4$. Anhydrous simple denotes without water.

The copper sulfate is the product of the action of sulfuric acid on metallic copper. The copper is oxidized by the sulfuric acid and water, and when the solution is evaporated the product formed is copper sulfate $Cu^{++} SO_4^{--}$.

If we make a solution of copper sulfate (the suffix ATE as in our case of a salt of copper), we mean a salt of the corresponding −IC (for example, sulfate from sulfuric acid). Let's look at a simple acid copper plating solution:

1 1/2 pounds copper sulfate $CuSO_4$.
3 1/2 ounces sulfuric acid H_2SO_4
1 gallon of distilled water H_2O

The $CuSO_4$ will disassociate in the water to give you Cu^{++} ions and SO_4^{--} ions (sulfate ion). Remember our sodium ions Na (+) and our chlorine ions Cl (−). We have the same proposition except that in place of sodium ions and chlorine ions there are copper ions and sulfate ions, oxygen, and hydrogen.

So what do we have in the solution? We have copper ions, Cu^{++}, hydrogen ions H^+, negative ions of sulfur and oxygen SO_4^{--}, and oxygen hydrogen ions OH^- ions (OH^- Hydroxide).

It looks like this when we add copper sulfate, $CuSO_4$, sulfuric acid, H2SO$_4$, and water, H$_2$O. We wind up with a real soup of dissociation:

Copper sulfate $CuSO_4 \rightleftharpoons Cu^{++} + SO_4^{--}$

Sulfuric acid $H_2SO_4 \rightleftharpoons 2H^+ + SO_4^{--}$

Water $H_2O \rightleftharpoons H^+ + OH^-$

The $\rightleftharpoons$ arrows simply indicate that the reaction or disassociation is reversable: $H_2O \rightarrow H^+ + OH^-$ can also go this way $H^+ + OH^- \rightarrow H_2O$.

OUR SOUP

See Fig. 1-23. In our case we have what is known as an acid electrolyte of various (+) and (−) ions. Because our metal ions consist of copper, we have what is known as a copper electrolyte or plating bath or an electroplating acid bath. The most common reference is to simply call it a copper bath or copper acid bath. I stated that an electrolyte can be decomposed by an applied electric current. Remember our double arrows $\rightleftharpoons$. Adding copper sulfate, sulfuric acid and water together moved everything over into our ionic soup this way $CuSO_4 \rightarrow Cu^{++} + SO_4^{--}$. If we apply a current properly we can decompose our soup.

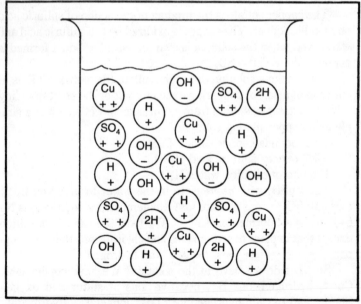

Fig. 1-23. A typical copper plating solution showing the various cations and anions swimming around in the electrolyte.

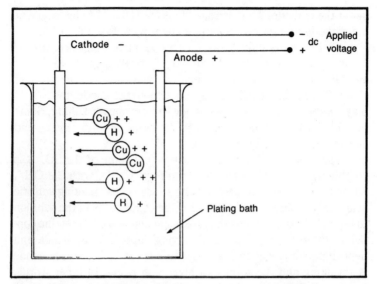

Fig. 1-24. Shows the hydrogen cations (+) and the copper cations (+ +) moving to the cathode to be reduced to copper atoms and hydrogen atoms.

What happens is simple. When we apply or pass a current through our solution of various (+) and (−) ions, the positively charged ions (cations) (in this case Cu^{++} and H^+) will move to the cathode, which is negative, where they discharge or gain the negative electrons that are missing as ions. Remember this is what made them + in the first place. When a Cu^{++} ion reaches the cathode, it picks up the two negative particles it needs to convert it from a copper ion to a copper atom. The H^+ ion picks up its missing electron and becomes a hydrogen gas atom.

In Fig. 1-24, we have a beaker that represents a plating tank and the electrolyte (our copper plating acid bath of disassociated ions), a copper anode and a cathode, and a dc electric source (battery, rectifier or generator).

In Fig. 1-24, I show only copper and hydrogen ions in the solution. Now, the copper $^{++}$ ions and hydrogen ions H^+ are attracted to the cathodes, which is negative in potential. Like charges repel and unlike charges attract. So they move through electrolyte and upon making contact gain the negative particles they need to be reduced from the ionic state to their correct atomic state. The hydrogen ion becomes a hydrogen gas atom and the copper ion becomes a copper atom. The copper plate at the cathodes will gain copper and grow as more and more copper ions are reduced to copper at the cathode. The hydrogen ions are reduced to hydrogen at the cathode and go off as gaseous hydrogen. See Fig. 1-25.

What happens at the anode (our copper plate which is positive)? Looking at the negative ions in our electrolyte, we have SO_4^{--} and OH^- ions. These, being negative, will travel to the positive anode. When they reach (make connection) the anode, the SO_4^{--} may combine with the copper anode to form copper sulfate. Some may be discharged and react with the water to form oxygen and sulfuric acid. See Fig. 1-26.

What is happening at the anode is that some of the SO_4^{--} is combining with the copper anode to form $CuSO_4$ with the OH^-, which have been neutralized. So the anode is busy making sulfuric acid, and the $CuSO_4$ is replenishing the copper ions in the solution to replace the copper ions that are being deposited as metallic copper at the cathode. We are dissolving copper at the anode and depositing copper at the cathode. In our case, the copper anode is shrinking and the copper cathode is growing. In other words, we are electroplating copper from a copper anode to a copper cathode.

You could substitute, in place of the copper cathode, an object made of another metal (tin, silver, iron, etc.). The action will be the same and the object at the minus pole will become coated with copper (copperplated).

If we replace the copper anode with an insoluble anode of car-

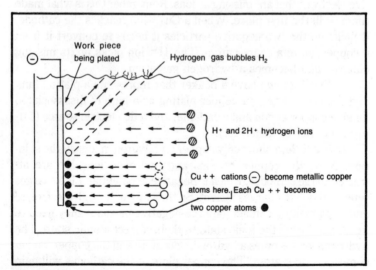

Fig. 1-25. The cathode (−) as the work is being plated.

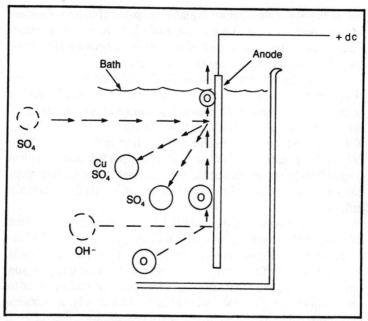

Fig. 1-26. The anode (+).

bon or stainless steel, we will simply plate out only the copper ions in our starting solution (bath). When they are all deposited as metallic copper at the cathode, the action stops because we are not replenishing the solution with new copper ions.

This is the reason we use a copper anode in a copper plating bath and a silver anode in a silver plating bath, etc. There are some exceptions to this rule which will be covered in the text as we move on. Chrome plating is an example.

Note: It's not all 100 percent efficient as we are using current in other reactions that may be considered as wasted (producing hydrogen gas, oxygen gas, etc.). If we substitute an object at the cathode that is nonmetallic or one that will not carry an electrical current (an insulator), we must make its surface conductive in order to plate it. This will be covered under plating nonconductors.

CLEARING THE AIR

You no doubt have noticed that you have SO_4^{--} and OH^- ions involved in the electrolyte. These combinations, called radicals, are simply defined as a group of atoms present in a series of compounds that maintain identity through chemical changes which affect the

23

rest of the molecules, but are usually incapable of independent existence. And they act like a single atom in forming a compound. They show valence as a part of a compound because they have gained or lost or shared electrons as a group.

If we go back to our compound NaCl, table salt, we have a compound of sodium and chlorine. We have two elements forming a compound. However, each element (sodium and chlorine) is capable of existing alone. With compounds such as H_2SO_4, $CuSO_4$, NaOH sulfuric acid, copper sulfate, and sodium hydroxide, you have SO_4 (called a sulfate radical) and you again see the sulfate radical coupled with copper. Sodium hydroxide (lye) is one sodium atom coupled with an OH radical. This OH radical is called a hydroxide radical.

Now let's look at Cu^{++} and SO_4^{--}. Sodium chloride, when disassociated in water to Na ions and Cl ions, gives Na^+ Cl^-. However, when we disassociate the copper ions from the SO_4 radical we come up with Cu^{++} SO_4^{--}. To understand what goes on, you have to understand what happens when you use sulfuric acid to form copper salt. Sulfuric acid is called a dibasic acid. It contains two replaceable hydrogen atoms per molecule.

Sulfuric acid H_2 SO_4 2 Hydrogen
Nitric acid HNO_3
Hydrochloric acid HCl   1 Hydrogen

Sulfuric acid may ionize only partially to form HSO_4^- ions or more completely to form your SO_4^{--} ions.

FURTHER STUDY

You really don't have to get excited about the chemistry of electroplating because with this book you can do it without the knowledge. However, the more you know about the subject you are working with the better off you are and a better job you will do. It's when you get into a problem with your process that knowledge of the inner workings pays off. It will pay you to do a little studying on basic chemistry especially on acids, bases, salts, oxidation and reduction (redox).

I will no longer dwell on the chemistry aspect of electroplating. The only chemistry will be a piece here and there where needed to clarify something for your safety.

THE PUREST SOLUTIONS

It is not necessary to compound your own plating salts to make up your solutions. They can be purchased but the more you do on your own the more rewarding and less expensive it becomes. You can make up some copper sulfate salt from some scrap copper. Make your plating solution and copper plate. You can buy copper plating solution ready-made or you can buy the copper salt, some distilled water (or rain water), and a jug of sulfuric acid. You can buy a plating tank from a supplier, a plastic container from a discount store, or gut an old auto battery and use the case for a tank. I could go on forever along this line.

Sophisticated equipment will not plate any better than homebrew equipment. It's know-how and attention to detail that counts.

Chapter 2

The Workshop

You are going to need a place to work, and of course the area depends on whether you are headed for a small-table setup or up from there. Let's assume you are going to do some plating (small stuff) for a hobby and maybe a little jewelry plating for others in order to pay for your hobby. If you start plating as a hobby and the word gets out that you can do small or jobbing plating, look out for sure. Customers will come out of the woodwork. If you don't look out, you will find that you are in business; there goes your hobby.

Commercial plating plants are highly mechanized and usually confine the plating to one or two types of work such as copper and chrome, gold, silver and rhodium, etc. Some specialize in lots of small parts while others work on only large items. Some specialize in plating only nonmetallic items such as baby shoes, plastic items, and leaves. You can turn out electroplating as good as a large commercial plant.

LOCATION

I have seen plating set up in the corner of a spare room, in a garage, and in numerous other places. Don't do the work in your house because of the toxic and corrosive nature of the chemicals involved. You need a safe, well-ventilated area with running water. If you set up shop at the end of your garage—unless it is walled off and the area exhausted off with a good fan and hood—in no time you will notice that your tools and your auto are rusting away at about 90 miles per hour.

If you must work in your basement or at the end of your garage, make it a separate room with a good hood and exhaust. Of course a nice separate building is great. I saw a slick little plating business, a real money-maker, in one of those 10- x -10 or 10- x -12 outside tool buildings you buy from the local lumberyard and they deliver it on a big truck.

BASIC SETUP

Let's go small. See Fig. 2-1. Now, let's look at the back wall from a more detailed view. See Fig. 2-2.

Take it piece by piece. You need a good sink to wash your glassware, scrub the pieces you are plating, wash your hands, and a good place to set your jugs when making up plating baths. The sink should be deep enough to give you lots of working room. The work table, your plating bench, should have a slight pitch to it and hang over one edge of the sink to take care of a spill and make it easy to wash the top of your bench. See Fig. 2-3.

Your hood should extend over the entire area of your bench and sink and be low enough to draw the fumes up and out. Of course you need head room. The hood should be made of wood or plastic due to the corrosive nature of some of the fumes. If you use a sheet-metal hood, black iron or galvanized iron, give it a couple of coats of asphalt or asphaltum. Asphaltum is a trade name for an asphalt paint that you can buy from your local paint supplier. You can melt some asphalt or roofing asphalt tar in a double boiler and use this to coat your hood. See Fig. 2-4.

Now, let's look at the exhaust system. You want to pipe from the hood and up and out with 4-inch ID PVC pipe. The hood suction can be accomplished with a shop vacuum. You don't want to pull the fumes through a conventional fan exhaust system because this pulls the fumes through the motor and in short order you will have corroded your motor windings away. Also, as plating generates some hydrogen gas you don't want this gas going through anything that could result in ignition of the hydrogen, causing an explosion. Every so often you hear of someone blowing up their auto battery by causing a spark, above the battery, igniting the hydrogen given off by the battery. When you plate, the little bubbles coming off of the cathode (the item you are plating) are H_2 hydrogen.

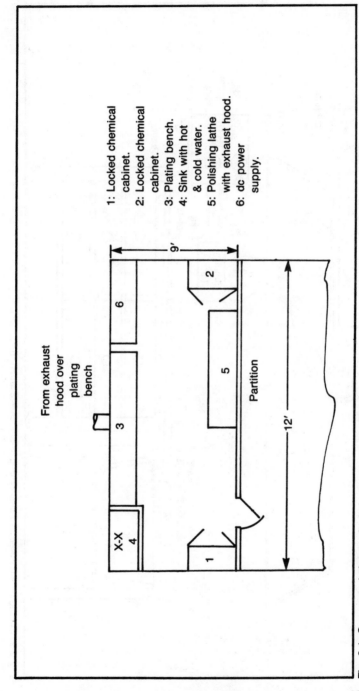

From exhaust hood over plating bench

9'

12'

Partition

1: Locked chemical cabinet.
2: Locked chemical cabinet.
3: Plating bench.
4: Sink with hot & cold water.
5: Polishing lathe with exhaust hood.
6: dc power supply.

Fig. 2-1. Compact plating works is in the back of a garage.

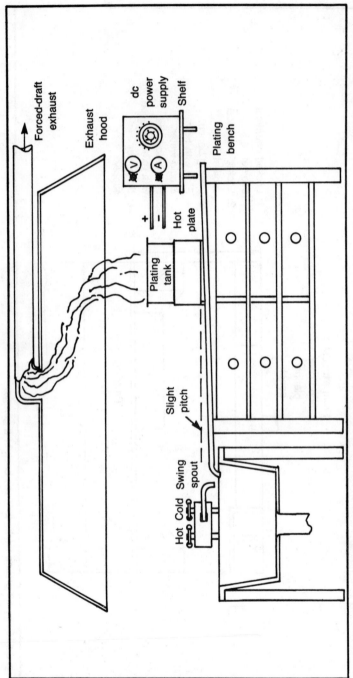

Fig. 2-2. Plating bench detail and sink arrangement. See 3 and 4 in Fig. 2-1.

30

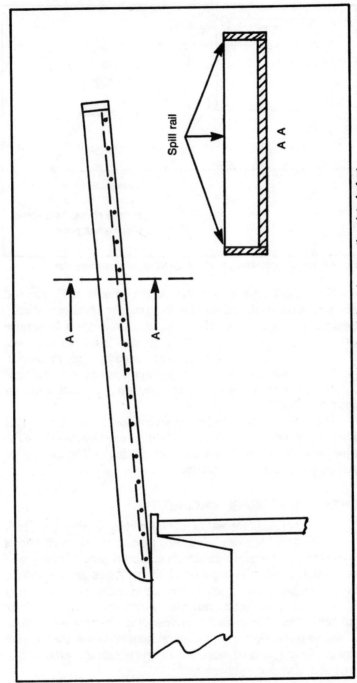

Fig. 2-3. Bench details show that spill rails will direct any spill into the sink and not on the plater's feet.

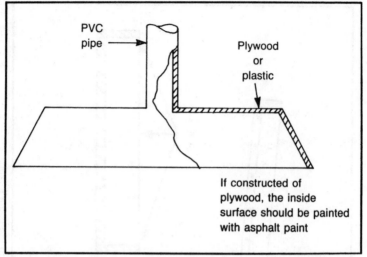

PVC pipe

Plywood or plastic

If constructed of plywood, the inside surface should be painted with asphalt paint

Fig. 2-4. Hood construction made of wood, plastic, or sheet steel.

Now, don't get alarmed because the amount of H_2 you will generate is minimal, and you are in no danger of collecting sufficient to cause a problem. However, as hydrogen is a flammable gas you want to exhaust it and avoid ignition. In a large operation, it is a problem and the tanks are exhausted by large systems.

By running a nozzle into your stack system, you can blow through this with your shop vac and create a good suction to your hood. See Fig. 2-5.

The outside stack should go up several feet above the roof. This will get any fumes high enough to be dispensed harmlessly to the wind. Also, height increases the draft efficiency. The top of your plating bench should be formica.

CHEMICAL STORAGE CABINETS

Some chemicals are not compatible with each other. See Chapters 3 and 4 on chemicals. You need to store the basic chemicals in one area and the acidic chemicals in another area in locked cabinets. Basic means the opposite of acidic. Bases include sodium hydroxide, potassium cyanide, sodium cyanide, etc. Keep away from sulfuric acid, nitric acid, and hydrochloric acid, etc. Never put any chemical in another container other than the one it came in originally. Never use a chemical without looking at the label before dispensing. Locked cabinets are obviously for the safety of children and unauthorized persons.

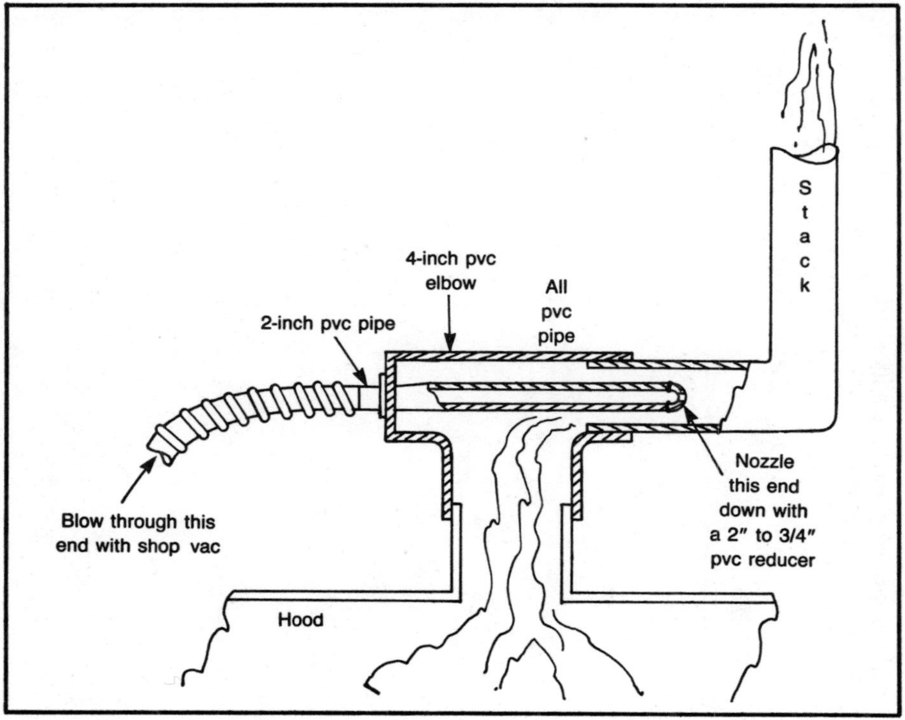

Fig. 2-5. Suction arrangement for fume hood.

Stack

Nozzle this end down with a 2" to 3/4" pvc reducer

All pvc pipe

4-inch pvc elbow

2-inch pvc pipe

Hood

Blow through this end with shop vac

33

SHOP SIZE AND ARRANGEMENT

Not knowing how big or small you are going to have to start your operation, it is impossible to spell out what you will need in any real detail. However, you will need running water, a sink, a bench, an exhaust system, and locked cabinets. Do this before you attempt to plate anything.

All you have to do is drop and break a small bottle of ammonia (ammonium hydroxide) and you will soon see that you need a good hood to exhaust the fumes. You won't have time to build one after the fact. Get a little nitric acid on your finger and you had better be in reach of a water faucet to flush it off at once. Have a good wall-hung fire extinguisher where you can grasp it. I'm not trying to scare you. Be prepared. Also, a nice, well-equipped, well-organized work area makes working not only safe, but a joy. And you will produce better-quality work.

Chapter 3

Hygiene and Safety

This is a little chapter of great importance. Electroplating is a chemical electrical proposition. Regardless of what type of chemicals you handle, hygiene is as important as your knowledge of the material with which you will be working. Every so often you will read where someone mixes a chloride bleach with ammonia or hydrogen peroxide, an acid or acid product, to clean a bathtub. They do this in a confined, poorly ventilated area. Bingo, they start up a chemical reaction that releases chlorine gas—a deadly toxin. Or some fellow cleans his carburator in a pan of gasoline (a chemical) in the kitchen (because it's cold outside) and the fumes are ignited by the pilot flame on the hot-water heater—and bang. You read of this often. Someone working with sodium hydroxide (lye) while not using gloves and in close quarters. They wind up severely burned due to a spill. Dump a solution of lye in an aluminum container and you produce tons of heat and hydrogen gas.

I am not trying to scare you, but you must play it safe. Get a rubber apron (wear it), get some rubber gloves (wear them), and get goggles or a face shield (use them).

Keep your work area clean and well organized. Don't let things get cluttered. Its a simple case of being smart. It is no different than pushing a short piece of wood through a circle saw with your fingers instead of a stick or operating a power saw without the guards and no face shield. You see it all the time.

CHEMICALS

Let's look at some of the chemicals with which you will be working. Some are basic (bases) and some are acetic (acids). A basic chemical is one that has the properties exactly opposite of an acetic chemical and can react with great violence when in contact with an acetic chemical.

If you were to add a very basic solution to an acid solution in order to neutralize it or to change the pH of the solution, there is a chemical reaction. The extent of the speed or violence of the reaction would depend on a number of conditions, how basic is the solution and how acetic the added solution is, the temperature of both solutions, and the speed and quantity involved.

If you want to neutralize, for example, a solution of nitric acid with ammonium hydroxide slowly, a little at a time, with a pause between additions to allow for the reaction to take place and things to cool down—you should have no problem. But go at it too fast and you have on your hands what we call high-speed chemistry. The reaction is of such a magnitude that great energy is released in a short span of time and it goes off like gun powder.

Metallic sodium reacts with great violence and speed. When it is dropped in water very rapid oxidation takes place between the oxygen atoms and the sodium atoms. In high-school chemistry, the teacher usually demonstrates this by dropping piece of sodium metal the size of a match head or smaller in a beaker of water. It produces sparks and lots of action by the release of energy produced by the chemical reaction. Drop a chunk of sodium the size of a pea or bean and you have an explosion.

Drano, your well-known household drain opener, is simply a mixture of sodium hydroxide (lye) and small aluminum chips. Everything is cool when the sodium hydroxide is anhydrous, Anhydrous means without water or moisture, and the aluminum chips are dry. Now mix this with water and everything breaks loose, producing (very rapidly) heat, hydrogen gas, and aluminum oxide +.

This is why you don't just dump the contents of the can in the drain. You use a tablespoon full, let the chemical reaction take place and subside, and then flush some water through. If the first dose did not do it, you try again with another dose.

THE P TRAP DANGER

Here's a spot where many hobbyists get into trouble by not thinking. this seems to be a trivial thing to even point out, but every so often someone gets hurt. What happens is this, you pour an acid solution down the drain without flushing it through with sufficient water. The solution retained in the trap becomes acetic. Some time later you pour a basic solution into the drain and you have just mixed a base and an acid together in the confines of the neck in the "P" trap. Boom! Up it comes all over the place. See Fig. 3-1. If you are unlucky enough to have your face in the line of fire, you could be injured badly. Of course this could be reversed (acid added to a base solution in the trap).

You are supposed to neutralize and dilute with a lot of water anything you flush down a drain. If your P trap is brass or copper with an acid solution, the metal will be attached and this could lead to an explosion plus a discharge of nitrous oxides from the drain.

Brownish red nitrous fumes, called dinitrogen tetraoxide, are a common by-product of the reaction of nitric acid with metals and organic materials. Not only are these fumes very toxic by inhalation, but they can react violently or explosively with a wide range of materials (alcohols, liquid ammonia, hydrocarbons). This is one of the reasons you must work under an exhaust hood and wear protective clothing.

STRONG BASES

There is a misconception that a strong base such as sodium hydroxide, potassium hydroxide, or ammonium hydroxide is much less dangerous than a strong acid such as nitric acid, hydrochloric acid, or sulfuric acid. This is not so by a long shot. A strong basic solution will take off more hide and a lot quicker than an equal amount of a strong acid solution.

ACID AND WATER

When acid is added to water the resulting reaction produces heat. If you add sulfuric acid to a small beaker of water you will find that upon touching the outside of the beaker it is getting quite warm. Add enough acid fast enough and sufficient heat can be generated very quickly and with a sufficient release of energy that the contents will boil over or the container will rupture or both.

Always add the acid to the water in small doses with enough time between additions to allow cooling off. Never add water to acid; it simply erupts with explosive force, throwing it out.

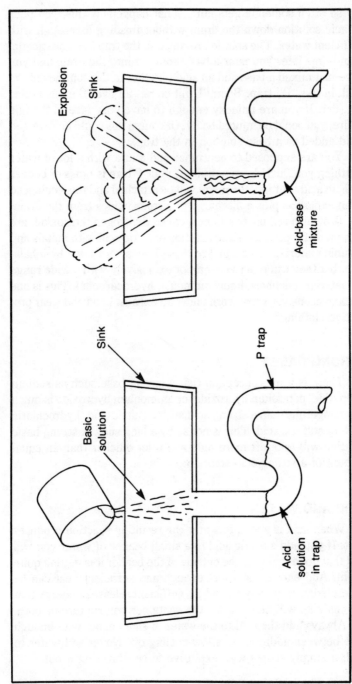

Fig. 3-1. The p trap danger of explosion or the release of toxic fumes.

HEATING

Most liquids can, under the proper conditions, be heated above their boiling temperature with no bubbling or apparent action indicating that they are in fact above their boiling point. You must get a liquid above its boiling point (slightly) before bubble initiation starts. When you heat a solution much higher than its boiling point without bubbles forming, you have what is called a superheated solution.

Should a bubble start to form in a superheated solution, it will grow almost instantaneously, resulting in a violent explosive eruption that can shatter the container. This is the usual cause when someone is scalded. Take a pan of milk on the stove where it is resting quietly with no vibration and being heated slowly. It can easily become super-heated, and when disturbed, such as moving it by the handle or sticking a spoon in it, it will boil over in a split second.

To prevent superheating, you should always use a few boiling stones or chips. these consist of pure silica fused and bonded to form stones. they have innumerable sharp projections for the release of vapor bubbles. They are available from your chemical supplier. You can use chips of broken test tubes or tubing as boiling chips. You should have enough involved that when the solution is boiling there is always some on the bottom even with the lifting action caused by boiling. You put them in to start with when the liquid is at room temperature. If you add them to a hot solution, you have the "spoon-in-the-milk" problem, only worse. See Fig. 3-2.

If you have an electric hot plate with a stirring motor, you simply place a stir bar in the liquid and keep the solution in motion with the bar. This setup consists of a hot plate arrangement whereby there is a magnet driven by a rheostat control. The magnet can be revolved over a large range of revolutions at the operator's will, with the rheostat control. The magnet is directly under the hot plate's heating surface. The spin bar is a plastic-covered iron bar. When it is placed in a beaker and the beaker is placed in the center of the hot plate, it is attracted to the magnet that lies under the hot plate's surface. When the magnet is rotated by its electric motor, the spin bar rotates also at the same rpm as the magnet. See Fig. 3-3.

Spin bars come in all sizes and shapes, as do the hot plates with magnet stirrers. They are not inexpensive, but if you can afford one it is worth it's weight in gold. You can use it to heat and stir to dissolve your salts when making up solutions.

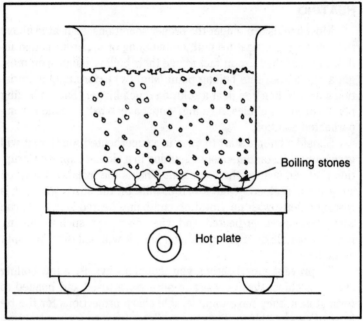

Fig. 3-2. Boiling stones prevent boil over or explosion due to superheating of a solution.

You can also use it to simply agitate a plating bath when plating small objects in a beaker. You can buy magnetic stirrers only with no heating element.

HEATING IN TEST TUBES

When heating in a test tube over a burner, heat slowly with the opening of the tube pointing away from you in case the test tube should decide to become a steam canon and project its contents out and across the room. Keep out of the line of fire. Keep the tube moving to prevent bumping. Never heat anything in glassware, beaker, flask, or test tube without first making sure that the outside of the container is dry. A beaker with its bottom wet can explode or burst by the steam generated between itself and the top of the heat source.

SMELLING

Your nose can save your life but it can also get you in trouble. Should you be in an area where you detect gas of some sort—natural gas, ammonia, chlorine, hydrogen sulfide, or sulfur dioxide—you

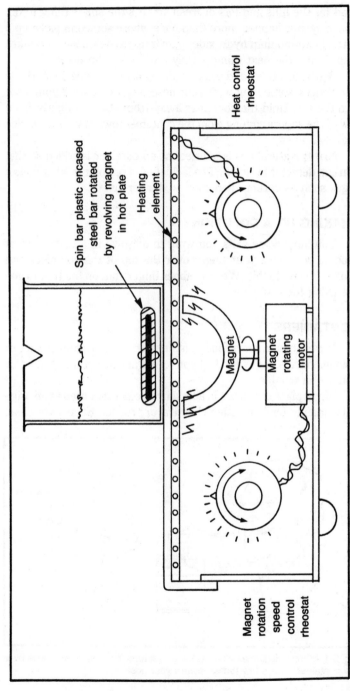

Fig. 3-3. Schematic of hot plate with spin bar motor to stir while heating.

41

head for the hills and lots of fresh air. It's the smart thing to do. I have seen it happen more than once where someone picks up a bottle of ammonium hydroxide, puts it up to their nose, and takes a sniff, and the next thing is they are flat on the floor.

Bottle, test tube, and beaker sniffing should not be done. If you must check something with your nose, you don't stick your nose into the act. Hold the container away from you and lightly fan a few of the vapors coming from the container toward your nose. See Fig. 3-4.

Note: Natural gas is odorless so an odorizer is added so that you can detect it by smell. The lack of odor or color is what makes a gas such as carbon monoxide so dangerous.

SHAKING UP A SOLUTION

You have some salts you want to dissolve in a bottle or test tube so you place your finger over the top of the container and shake. We all do this. Wear a rubber finger stall on the thumb you are using for a stopper.

CONTAINERS

Never, never use a food container or a water glass to mix or hold chemicals of any kind. If you forget and next thing you know you are in trouble.

Never place chemicals in another container that used as an original container for some other chemical or product. Even if you clean

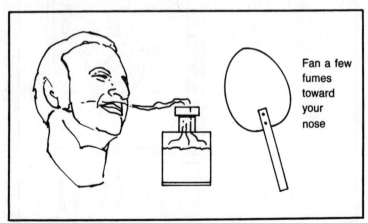

Fan a few fumes toward your nose

Fig. 3-4. When smelling a bottle beaker or test tube, don't stick your nose over the container. Fan a few fumes toward your nose.

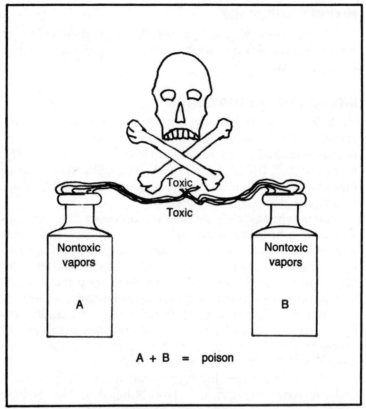

Fig. 3-5. Two nontoxics together make a toxic.

out the new container, it can lead to a mix up. Keep your labels in good condition and always read the label carefully each time you dispense something.

Acid bottles are usually color-coded with screw caps, sulfuric acid "yellow," nitric acid "red," hydrochloric acid "blue," etc., but don't count on this because the caps could get transposed accidently (you could do it). Look at the label; is it sulfuric acid or sulfurous acid? Never eat anything in your shop.

When using wet or dry chemicals, select the chemical you want to use, weigh out or measure out the desired amount, close the container, return it to its storage place, and then select the next chemical needed. Don't open more than one container at a time. If you were to have two chemicals open side by side that are noncompatible, they could get knocked over and make contact, or the vapors could simply get together causing a reaction. See Fig. 3-5.

MIXING COMPOUNDS

You don't ever mix x and y to see what will happen. You might get a real surprise. Know what you are doing and what reaction, if any, will take place.

INCOMPATIBLE COMPOUNDS

This is a little tough to explain. If you were to look up in any chemical reference as to what is incompatible with what other compounds, you could get confused. Let's look at a typical entry: Hydrochloric Acid (HC1) (muriatic acid). You will find an equeous solution is corrosive, irritating and poisonous, and the fumes are irritating to the mucous membranes.

It is not combustible in air, however. In contact with most common metals, hydrogen is evolved (which is an explosive gas) is evolved. This could lead one to believe that you would be crazy to use this acid to dissolve or digest a bit of copper metal in order to get some copper chloride salts or for whatever purpose. There is little danger of producing sufficient hydrogen to cause threatening conditions while working with small or medium quantities under an exhaust hood or outside. If you dump several pounds of copper turnings into a crock of HC1 in a confined area and where there is a pilot light, there will be an explosion.

Now, there are some items, chemicals, and compounds that— under no conditions—should be brought together. The resulting combination could be a real health hazard as a toxic gas or highly sensitive explosive compound.

Chapter 4

Chemicals Used in Plating

You don't have to be a chemist to do top-quality electroplating. It is, however, a decided advantage to have an understanding of what is going on and why. I could not begin to cover the chemistry of plating in this volume (that's another book). Most basic texts on general chemistry will give you a real running start, but you don't have to study chemistry to do top-quality plating. Simply follow the instructions and the formulas as given and you will get excellent results. Everything given here has been tried and proven.

ACIDS

Defined as a large class of chemical substances whose water solutions have one or more of the following properties:

☐ Sour taste.
☐ Will turn litmus dye red.
☐ Ability to react with and dissolve certain metals to form salts of the metal dissolved. An example is copper dissolved in sulfuric acid produces, when the H_2O is removed, copper sulfate salt.
☐ When put into solution with water, ionization takes place so that most of the hydrogen forms H_3O + ions.

Acids are classified as strong or weak acids according to the hydrogen ion concentration. Hydrochloric acid HC1, nitric acid,

HNO_3, and sulfuric acid H_2SO_4 are strong acids. These acids (mineral acids) are highly corrosive to human tissue. These acids also have the ability to replace the hydrogen atom with a metal. Example: If you cover some small pieces of zinc metal with a dilute solution of sulfuric acid, it will begin to bubble—giving off hydrogen (gas). The hydrogen given off is replaced by the zinc (giving you zinc sulfate). So now you have an acid radical and a metal. This combination of the acid radical (formed by the acid giving up its hydrogen) and the metal which took the hydrogen's place is known as a metal salt.

Metal + acid radical = metal salt. Zinc metal + H_2SO_4 = $ZnSO_4$. $7H_2O$. Note: The . $7H_2O$ in our formula is simply water of crystallization. If we crystallize the salt out of our solution, we have the metallic salt of zinc and sulfur.

If you use a nitric acid solution to dissolve the zinc in place of sulfuric acid, you wind up with a zinc nitrate solution from which you could crystallize out the zinc metal salt $ZN(NO_3)_2$. $6H_2O$. With hydrochloric acid, you would come up with a final zinc salt that would be zinc chloride, $ZnCl_2$.

Note. It is the ability to be able to produce metal salts that can be dissolved in water where ionization takes place, leaving the metallic (+) ions free to swim around, that makes electroplating possible.

The plating bath, called an electrolyte, is defined as a compound in a solution that conducts an electric current and is simultaneously decomposed by it. The current is not carried by electrons; it is carried by the ions. Plating electrolytes can be acids or bases.

BASES OR ALKALIES

A base is exactly opposite of an acid turning litmus blue. Equal proportions of acid solutions and alkaline solutions will neutralize each other with the evolution of heat. Like acids, bases can be any one of a large family of materials with one or more of the following properties: bitter taste; slippery feeling in solution; ability to neutralize acids; turns litmus blue.

Sodium hydroxide, potassium hydroxide, and ammonium hydroxide are water soluble and they undergo ionization to produce hydroxyl ion (OH –) in considerable concentration. Sodium hydroxide, potassium hydroxide, and ammonium hydroxide are strong bases (alkalies). Potassium hydroxide is often called caustic potash. Sodium hydroxide is often called caustic soda or lye.

Both sodium hydroxide and potassium hydroxide are widely used to clean and degrease work to be plated. These materials readily absorb moisture from the air and must be kept in tightly closed containers. If left open, the chemicals will become damp and cake. As they absorb carbonic acid gas from the air, the chemicals slowly will be converted to a carbonate and will be useless for cleaning. When sodium or potassium hydroxide is used for degreasing, it converts the grease to soap (grandma's lye soap).

AMMONIA

Another base is ammonia (solution). Ammonia gas is dissolved in water to make the ammonia solution. It is purchased in various strengths. The water solution of ammonia is sometimes called spirits of Hartshorn, but its most common name is ammonium hydroxide (NH_4OH). A solution containing 29.4 percent ammonia is a stable solution. It is also a strong solution (very, very basic). Other names it goes by are ammonium hydrate and aqua ammonia.

It is best to buy ammonium hydroxide solution below a 25 percent solution. Above 25 percent, in warm weather, pressure can build up in the container. This results in problems when the cap is removed. Chemical solutions run as high as 35 percent ammonia. Ammonium hydroxide is irritating to the skin, eyes, and respiratory system. Avoid breathing the vapor.

QUICK LIME

The prefix quick means alive or active. Quick lime is calcium oxide (unslacked lime) (CaO) called calcia or caustic lime. With the addition of water, it becomes hot and decomposes or crumbles into slacked lime. Quick lime is also used as a cleaner in plating.

VIENNA LIME

Quick lime combined with powdered magnesia is used as a polishing material.

ACETATES

Copper acetate is made up of minute silky crystals that are either pale green or bright blue in color, and is produced by the action of acetic acid on copper often called verdiglis. Moderately toxic, it is only slightly soluble in water but soluble in acids, ammonia and cyanide solutions. In plating it is used in copper and brass baths and for chemical coloring of metals.

LEAD ACETATE

Lead acetate, often called sugar of lead, consists of white crystal flakes. Like copper acetate, it is produced by the action of acetic acid on lead or litharge (lead oxide). Lead acetate, like most lead compounds, is highly toxic by way of ingestion, inhalation, and absorption by the skin. Keep this chemical in tightly closed containers. It is water soluble and it is used in various plating solutions and coloring baths.

CARBONATES

A carbonate is a salt of carbonic acid (H_2CO_3). Carbonic acid (bubble water) is a weak acid produced when carbon dioxide is dissolved in water. A small portion of the carbon dioxide dissolved in the water forms H_2CO_3. Some metal carbonates, used in plating baths, are copper carbonate $Cu_2 (OH)_2 CO_3$ and are toxic by ingestion. Nickel carbonate $NiCO_3 . 2Ni (OH)_2 . 4H_2O$ is toxic as a dust or powder and it is also flammable.

Potassium carbonate also called potash, pearl ash, solutions of potassium carbonate will irritate the skin. And, of course our old familiar washing soda sodium carbonate and bicarbonate of soda.

CHLORIDES

With chlorides, remember that the suffix *ide* denotes a compound that is binary, consisting of two elements or radicals combined to produce a compound. Therefore, a chloride would be a compound of chlorine plus some other element such as metallic sodium and chlorine as NaCl sodium chloride (table salt).

Chlorine will couple up with hundreds of other elements to produce a very, very large family of chlorides. The reason for this is that the chlorine atom looks like Fig. 4-1.

The nucleus contains 17 protons (+) and you have two electrons in the K shell, eight in the L shell, and seven in the M shell. The chlorine atom, needing only one electron to complete its outer shell, is actively seeking the extra electron. Under the proper conditions, it will grab one from just about any unwary atom with one electron hanging out there. An example is a copper atom that has two electrons in the K shell, eight in the L shell, 18 in the M shell. A lone electron flying around in the N shell is easy prey for the

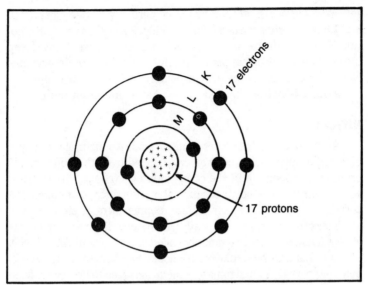

Fig. 4-1. Schematic diagram of a chlorine atom.

chlorine to scoop up and form a nice compound of copper chloride, a brownish yellow powder or green deliquescent crystals. Now, let's look at a few of the chlorides used in plating baths.

Ammonium Chloride. Also called sal ammoniac, ammonium chloride is widely used to increase the electrical conductivity of a plating bath. It is also very active cleaning agent.

Copper Chloride. Copper plating baths.

Gold Chloride. This compound is the ingredient in most gold plating solutions. It is available as crystals of an orange-yellow color carrying some free acid, and as a brown crystalline mass which is acid free. This is the salt you should use. When we get to cyanides, you will understand why the acid-free gold chloride is preferred. Keep it in tightly capped bottles.

Nickel Chloride. A green powder or crystals, this powder is preferred as it contains less free acid. *Note*: When making up a nickel bath and you get a yellow precipitate (fall out), add a few drops of hydrochloric acid. This will correct the problem by putting the precipitate back into the bath.

Silver Chloride. A white powder, silver chloride—when exposed to light—progressively turns darker and darker. The action is the basis of your photographic papers and films. It is not soluble in water but is very soluble in ammonium hydroxide and potassium cyanide solutions. Here's one chloride that is easy to make yourself from old scrap sterling silver or pure silver. See Chapter 9.

Tin Chloride. Called stannous chloride or tin salts. Tin chloride is used in tin baths as well as brass and bronze baths. Keep the container tightly capped. If a solution of tin chloride becomes cloudy, add a few drops of hydrochloric acid to clear it up.

Zinc Chloride. Is used in zinc baths and brass baths.

NITRATES

A nitrate is a salt or ester of nitric acid. An example is copper digested in nitric acid and then crystallized from the liquid would produce a copper salt of the composition $Cu(NO_3)_2 \cdot 3H_2O$ called copper nitrate. The suffix *ate* indicates a chemical compound of a corresponding acid (copper sulfate, copper nitrate, etc.).

Mercury Nitrate. A heavy yellow powder mercury nitrate is an extremely toxic, commonly called mercurous nitrate $HgNO_3 \cdot 2H_2O$, that can be explosive if shocked or heated. It is used in quicking baths for amalgamating metal surfaces to be plated. Mercury nitrate solution is made by dissolving a small amount of mercury in a dilute nitric acid solution. If rubbed or brushed on a metal surface, the metal will take on a thin coating of mercury. This is accomplished by ion exchange. A minute amount of the surface will exchange places in the acid with the mercury, depositing the mercury in its place. More on this later.

POTASSIUM NITRATE

Also called saltpeter or niter, potassium nitrate is used as an oxidizer to supply oxygen. It is the element in black gun powder that supplies the oxygen of combustion for the sulfur and charcoal.

SILVER NITRATE

A silver salt silver nitrate is also called lunar salt. It is highly toxic and a strong irritant to the skin. As you have probably already deduced, silver nitrate is produced by the action of a dilute nitric acid solution on metallic silver and then crystallized. The crystals are colorless and transparent but will change color from gray to grayish black when exposed to light. Keep it tightly capped in a dark bottle away from light. At one time, lunar salts in stick form were used as a septic stick.

When making up a solution of silver nitrate crystals, you must use distilled, chlorine-free water. If you use tap water, any metallic salts in the water will drop or precipitate the silver out as metallic silver. If there is any chlorine in the water, the silver will drop out as a silver chloride.

You will be using silver nitrate in silver plating baths and in forming a conducting film on nonmetallic items you want to plate.

PHOSPHATES

Sodium phosphate, called sodium metaphosphate ($NaPO_3$), is a nontoxic phosphate used in gold plating solutions.

Another phosphate, sodium pyrophosphate, is used in gold, tin and nickel baths. The prefix pyro denotes a chemical substance obtained by heating pyro boric acid produced by heating boric acid. A phosphate would be a compound containing phosphorous atoms.

SULFATES

Ammonium Sulfate. Mostly used to increase the conducting power of some plating solutions, ammonium sulfate is water soluble and it evaporates when heated.

Copper sulfate is used in copper baths. The crystals should be nice and blue. When copper sulfate crystals are contaminated, they will be off color. If it is green in color, it is an indication it is contaminated with iron sulfate and would be unsuitable for use in a copper bath. Copper sulfate is also called blue vitriol or blue stone.

Iron sulfate is a sulfate of iron used in iron plating baths. Due to its green color it is called green vitriol. It is also used to precipitate gold from solutions such as spent gold baths.

Nickel ammonium sulfate is a nickel ammonia sulfur compound called a double sulfate of nickel and ammonia or double salt: $NiSO_4 . (NH_4)_2 SO_4 . 6H_2O$.

A double salt is when you get a compound formed by crystallization from a solution containing both of them. If you have a solution containing nickel sulfate and ammonium sulfate, for example, the crystallized product from that solution would be a (double salt) compound of $NiSO_4$ 1 salt + $(NH_4)_2 SO_4$, (the second salt plus six molecules of water of crystallization).

Similarly if you dissolved potassium sulfate and aluminum sulfate in solution together and then crystallized the product out, you would have a double salt: $K_2SO_4 . AL_2 (SO_4)_2 . 2H_2O$. This is a double salt or potassium aluminum sulfate.

The nickel ammonium sulfate is pale green in color and is widely used in nickel plating baths.

Potassium aluminum, sulfate mentioned above in our examples

of double salts, is more commonly called alum and is clear crystals (no color). It is used in zinc baths.

Sodium sulfate Na_2SO_4 . lo H_2O, called sodium sulfate decahydrate, means 10 molecules of water .10 H_2O. It is more commonly called Glauber's salt, and is used in many different plating baths as colorless transparent crystals or powder.

Sodium sulfite Na_2SO_3 is made up of white crystals or powder with a sulfurous taste. It is sometimes used in a plating bath to increase the acidity to increase its conducting power.

Note: You may have noticed that one compound is sodium sulfate and one compound is sodium sulfide: sodium sulfate Na_2SO_4; sodium sulfate $NaSO_4$; sodium sulfite $NaSO_3$.

The suffix *ate* indicates a salt with metal or a radical in the highest oxidation state. The oxidation state is the number of electrons that must be added in order to neutralize the electrical charge.

The suffix *ite* indicates an intermediate oxidation state of a metal salt analogous to -ous for acids. Sodium sulfite containing one less oxygen atom than the sulfate.

Zinc Sulfate. Zinc sulfate is made up of odorless, colorless crystals that have a metallic taste. It is an astringent $ZnSO_4$. $7H_2O$ produced by the action of sulfuric acid on zinc metal or zinc oxide. A very good soldering flux, in plating it is used in zinc baths, brass baths, and pickling baths.

SULFIDES

Sulfide compounds are characterized by their rotten-egg odor. Don't store sulfides with other chemicals because they can be contaminated with sulfur or convert them into sulfides.

Antimony sulfide is used in antimony baths and in chemical coloring solutions. Ammonium sulfide, iron sulfide, and potassium sulfide are used to generate hydrogen sulfide gas by the addition of hydrochloric or sulfuric acid.

Figure 4-2 shows the reaction is iron sulfide + hydrochloric acid = ferrous chloride + hydrogen sulfide. $FeS + 2 HCL \rightarrow FeCl_2 + H_2S \uparrow$. If sulfuric acid is used, the formula and products would be iron sulfide + sulfuric acid = ferrous sulfate + hydrogen sulfide or $FeS + H_2SO_4 \rightarrow FeSO_4 + H_2S \uparrow$.

Hydrogen sulfite H_2S is a very valuable compound (gas) for the metal plater due to its wide range of uses. Metal coloring means metallizing nonmetallic objects so they are conductive and can be electroplated. Hydrogen sulfite can be used to precipitate metal

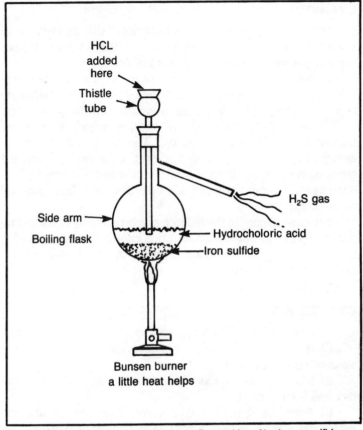

Fig. 4-2. Simple lab set up to generate small quantities of hydrogen sulfide gas.

values from solutions or spent plating baths. It is a strong reducing agent. If you bubble H_2S gas through an acetic solution containing metal ions, it will precipitate the metal out as a metal sulfide. H_2S can be purchased by the tank. A small lecture bottle will last for quite some time. More on its use later.

TARTRATES

Antimony potassium tartrate is a common tartar emetic used in antimony baths. Potassium bitartrate or cream of tartar is widely used in plating baths, making up tin and silvering pastes, and in some scratch brush work.

Potassium sodium tartrate (Rochelle salt) is a salt of tartaric acid used for copper baths and silvering mirrors for plating.

CYANIDES

You will be using both sodium cyanide NaCN and potassium cyanide KCN. These two cyanide compounds are extremely toxic when ingested; even small amounts are deadly.

They are, like most toxic substances, quite harmless when properly used by persons experienced in their use. They are both high-tonnage compounds widely used in industry for many purposes.

The mining industry uses large tonnages of cyanide for the extraction of metallic values from ore. The commercial plating industry also uses large quantities of cyanide for plating baths and stripping baths. If you keep in mind the rules and practices for handling cyanide compounds and don't deviate from them, you will be in no danger.

You must memorize the following facts regarding cyanide compounds solutions. You should post this information on the wall in back of your bench as a constant reminder. I have used cyanide safely for over 45 years.

CYANIDE RULES

☐ Cyanide is deadly even in very small amounts taken orally.

☐ It is deadly when allowed to enter the body through abrasions or cuts in the skin.

☐ It poses a serious risk of poisoning by inhalation, skin contact and if swallowed.

☐ Acids and Cyanide. Never, never, never add acid to a cyanide, a cyanide compound, a cyanide salt (metal salt) or any cyanide solution. Cyanide and acid are incompatible because they produce deadly HCN, hydrogen cyanide, hydrocyanic gas. This poison is used in gas chambers and is extremely deadly.

☐ Keep acids stored on one end of the shop and cyanides stored on the other end of the shop—in locked cabinets.

☐ Always work under a well-exhausted hood when you use cyanides.

☐ Wear rubber gloves, a face shield and a rubber apron.

☐ Keep acid plating baths isolated from cyanide plating baths.

☐ If you spill cyanide solutions, scatter bleaching powder liberally over the spillage or dilute with a strong water solution of sodium hypochlorite. Mop up the spill and allow it to stand for 24 hours before running to waste with lots of water.

If you spill solid cyanides, swab it up and place it in a container with a large volume of water in which you can render it innocuous by adding an excess or sodium hypochlorite solution. Let stand for 24 hours and run to waste with lots of water.

Bleaching powder is Chlorinated lime. Some bleaching powders are a mixture of calcium chloride and calcium hypochlorite.

Sodium Hypochlorite is also called sodium ocychlorite, NaOCl. The water solution is called Javel water.

The percentage weight of metal in a salt will vary depending on whether the salt is a hydrous salt or whether the salt is anhydrous. See Tables 4-1 and 4-2. Hydrous would simply mean the salt contains some water of crystallization. For example, zinc sulfate $ZnSO_4 .7 H_2O$ or a zinc sulfate containing 7 molecules of water. The percent of zinc in this salt would be 22.7. Taking the same salt zinc sulfate (anhydrous) $Zn SO_4$, the percent of zinc in this salt, which is minus the $7H_2O$, would be 40.4 percent.

I have not designated in the salt listings whether they are hydrous or anhydrous, which could give you a variance in the metal content.

Let's go back and look at *ous* and *ic* again, and let's look at the difference between ferrous chloride salt and ferric chloride salt. The iron atom consists of 26 protons (+) and 26 electrons (–). See Fig. 4-3.

If we couple the iron atoms with chlorines, the chlorine atom that has 7 electrons in its outermost shell is looking for an electron to fill this shell to give it completeness. If two chlorine atoms hook up with one iron atom—the iron atom having two electrons in its outer shell it can donate—you have a compound of ferrous chloride $FeCl_2$. The iron atom has a + + charge as it still has 26 (+)

Table 4-1. Cyanide Metallic Salts.

Plating Baths and the Percentage of Metal In Them	
Cadmium cyanide Cd $(CN)_2$	68.3% Cd
Copper cyanide CuCn	71% Cu
Copper potassium cyanide $K_2Cu (CN)_3$	26.3%
Copper sodium cyanide $Na_2 Cu (CN)_3$	26.3% Cu
Gold cyanide AnCN	88.3% Au
Gold potassium cyanide K Au $(CN)_2$	68.3% Au
Gold sodium cyanide Na Au$(CN)_2$	72.5% Au
Silver cyanide AgCN	80.5% Ag
Silver potassium cyanide K Ag $(CN)_2$	54.2% Ag
Silver sodium cyanide Na Ag $(CN)_2$	59.2% Ag
Zinc cyanide Zn $(CN)_2$	55.7% Zn

Table 4-2. Acid Metallic Salts Used in Plating Baths.

Metallic Salts	Percentage of Metal
Cadmium chloride $2CdCl_2$	49.3% Cd
Cadmium sulfate $3CdSO_4$	43.3% Cd
Cobalt chloride $CoCl_2$	24.8% Co
Cobalt sulfate $CoSO_4$	21.0% Co
Copper chloride $CuCl_2$	37.3% Cu
Copper sulfate $CuSO_4$	25.5% Cu
Ferric (iron) chloride $FeCl_3$	20.6% Fe
Ferric sulfate $Fe_2(SO_4)_3$	27.9% Fe
Ferrous ammonium sulfate $FeSO_4 \cdot (NH_4)_2 SO_4$	14.2% Fe
Note: Here you have a double salt $FeSO_4 \cdot (NH_4)_2 SO_4$	
Ferrous chloride $FeCl_2$	20.1% Fe
Ferrous sulfate $FeSO_4$	20.1% Fe
Gold chloride $AuCl$	58% Au
Nickel chloride $NiCl_2$	24.7% Ni
Nickel sulfate $NiSO_4$	22.3% Ni
Silver chloride $AgCl$	75% Ag
Silver nitrate $AgNO_3$	63.5% Ag
Silver sulfate Ag_2SO_4	34.6% Ag
Tin chloride (Stannous Chloride) $SnCl_2$	52.6% Sn
Tin sulfate $SnSO_4$	55.3% Sn
Zinc sulfate $ZnSO_4$	22.7% Zn

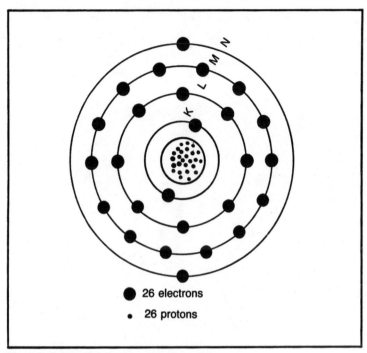

Fig. 4-3. Schematic diagram of an iron atom.

protons in its nucleus, but has lost two electrons, giving a net gain of two pluses.

If conditions are right, another chlorine could come along and pick off an electron from the m shell, leaving it with 13 electrons. Now you have an iron atom that has given up three electrons to satisfy three chloring atoms. You have an iron atom that is Fe + + + or a higher state of oxidation. This salt would be called ferric chloride as opposed to ferrous chloride. They are basically the same. Both compounds are iron and chlorine. However, one would react differently than the other in a chemical reaction due to the different oxidation states: sulfuric acid H_2SO_4; sulforous acid H_2SO_3.

I have not detailed all the chemicals mentioned in this book, but I have touched on the basic, most-used ones. Each chemical is described as it crops up in the text that follows.

Chapter 5

Current Supply

You must have a source of dc current for plating work. Your choices depend on how heavy you are going to get into electroplating. If small and only an occasional piece is going to be made, then a 6-volt, lead-acid automobile battery will suffice. However, such a battery will have to be recharged from time to time. You can use a small battery charger or the battery can be taken to a service station. Most battery chargers do a good job of charging; a trickle charge overnight usually restores the battery for use.

Some electroplaters advocate using a small battery charger as the plating current source. It is not, in most cases, a good current source because most of them are half-wave rectifiers. They deliver a pure dc current rather than a pulsating, intermittent current. A battery is pure uninterrupted dc. See Fig. 5-1.

You could simply hook the old, round 1.5-volt batteries in series to give you a 6-volt dc source or use one 6-volt dry battery. See Fig. 5-2.

For small objects with very little surface area to be plated one at a time with copper, gold, or silver there is very little current drain involved. The dry battery setup will work surprisingly well for quite a while before the dry battery or batteries are shot.

DRY RECTIFIER

There are available a wide range of sizes and types of dc dry

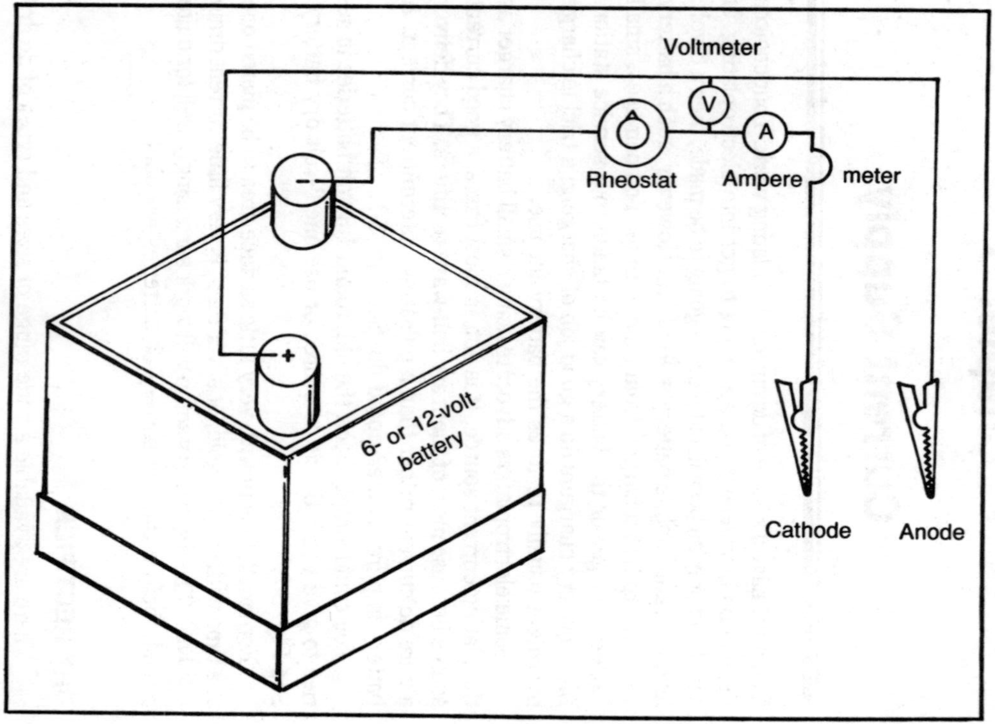

Fig. 5-1. An auto or motorcycle wet storage battery makes a good source for plating on a small scale.

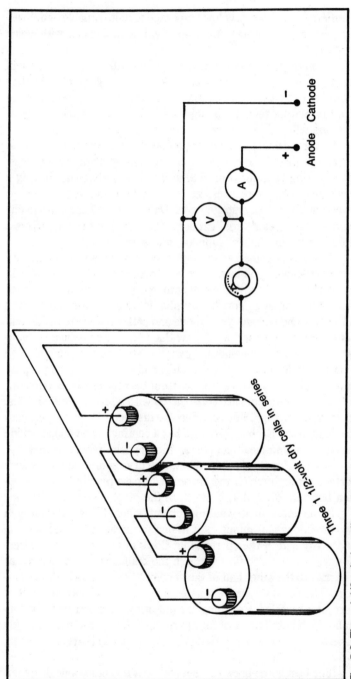

Fig. 5-2. Three 1 1/2-volt dry cells connected in series used for light plating.

61

rectifiers from extremely low amperage to units capable of delivering very large amperage. A dry rectifier is a good choice with which to start.

If you buy a rectifier with a capacity of 10 volts, 50 amps will serve you over a large variety of work. Most jewelry tool and hobby shops have these at a reasonable price (some below $100). The life of a dry plating rectifier is unlimited. Even a relatively inexpensive one will last for years.

I have a 10-volt, 75-ampere (copper oxide rectifier) that is at least 35 years old and still going strong. The advantage of purchasing a plating rectifier (Fig. 5-3) is that it's ready to go, having a rheostat to control the voltage, a volt meter and ampere meter. Swest Inc., 10803 Composite Drive, Dallas, Texas 75220, will gladly send you a jeweler's tool catalog. Their supply catalog covers a wide variety of platers, supplies, and solutions.

There is a decided advantage in purchasing a power unit (dry rectifier) because you have your power source in a nice clean package complete with a volt meter, ampere meter, and a rheostat to control the voltage. You simply plug in your rectifier in the wall (110 volts) and connect your anode and cathode leads to the dc output terminals on your unit. Throw the units switch, adjust the voltage, and you are in business. Any other way you are going to have to have a volt meter, ampere meter, and a rheostat. The purpose of a rectifier is to convert alternating current to direct current.

The dry rectifiers are constructed with a series of metal discs. In a simple copper oxide rectifier, the discs consist of copper discs and lead discs. Each copper disc has a coating of red copper oxide on one face and clean copper on the opposite face. Fig. 5-4.

The electrical principle behind the dry rectifier is a boundary surface through which the current will pass readily in one direction but with difficulty, if at all, in the other direction.

If you apply an alternating current (which flows alternately in two directions plus minus, plus minus ac current 60 cycles per second), only half of the current that flows in the appropriate direction will continue to flow through the boundary, which serves as a barrier to the other half of the current. This results in direct current. The rectifier can be a half-wave rectifier if only one-half of current is rectified. Resulting in a pulsating direct current (not continuous). If both halves of the alternating current are rectified, you have a full wave rectifier that is a continuous dc current. See Fig. 5-5.

The best home-brew current source is an automobile dc gener-

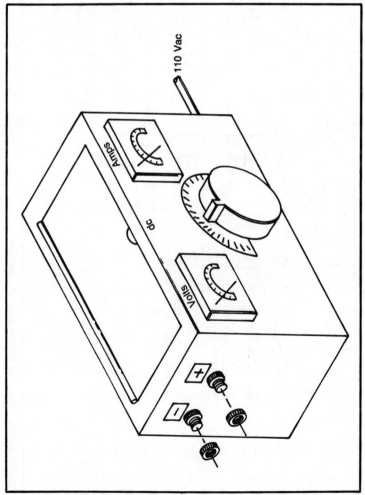

Fig. 5-3. A commercial dry rectifier for electroplating.

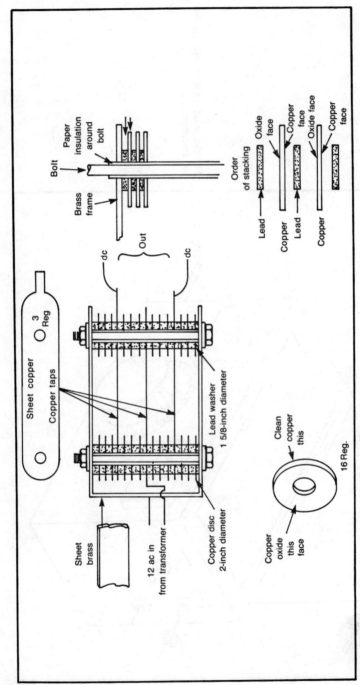

Fig. 5-4. Construction of a copper oxide dry rectifier.

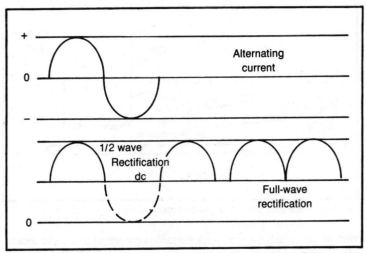

Fig. 5-5. Wave forms alternating current. Half-wave and full-wave direct current.

ator driven by a 1/4-horse power 1700 rpm motor. (Not an alternator.) This can be obtained from any junkyard. See Fig. 5-6.

The motor generator setup will cost you a few bucks, but it is trouble free with a long, long life and will deliver good dc current with sufficient amperage capacity to do a wide variety of work.

You should have some control over your voltage in all cases. Here you need a rheostat (variable resistance). You can purchase one from any electrical supply house or make a homemade one. See Fig. 5-7.

A saltwater rheostat can be made using a wooden or plastic tank full of saltwater with two moveable lead plates. The closer the plates are together the more voltage will flow. The voltage is controlled by varying the distance between the plates.

It is important that you understand what is going on chemically. You can electroplate without the foggiest notion on what is taking place. However, the more knowledge you have the simpler and much more interesting the work. Also the more you understand about what's going on the easier it is to spot and correct a problem that might pop up during a plating operation.

Remember you have the metal to be plated in a solution as an ion of that metal. In this ionic state, it is short one or more (−) electrons, making its electrical potential or charge (+). Unlike charged particles, ions attract each other.

The cathode (−) will attract the (+) charged ion to it where it can gain or pick up its one or more missing (−) electrons and re-

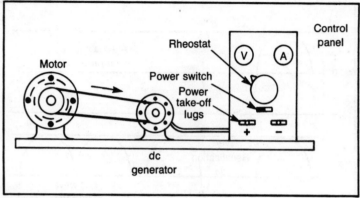

Fig. 5-6. Motor and generator power supply setup.

vert or be reduced back to its metallic or normal state. An example is copper ion Cu^{++}, plus 2 (−) electrons = $Cu°$ or copper metal at the cathode.

VALENCE VERSUS ELECTRICAL CHARGE

Let's clear the air on (+) valence (−) valence (+) electrical potential and (−) electrical potential. It sometimes can be confusing. When the reference is to valence (+) or (−), this only indicates the amount of electrons an atom can donate to a reaction or other atoms can accept. In both cases, when we refer to an atom as having a (+) or (−) valence we are not referring to its electrical

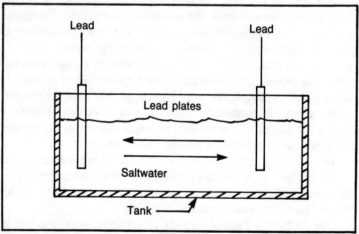

Fig. 5-7. A simple home made saltwater rheostat.

potential or charge at all. Plus is excess. Minus is a shortage.

Elements are in their normal state (neutral) as far as electrical potential is concerned. It is when they enter into a chemical reaction and in doing so gain or lose negative electrons that they become positive or negative electrically.

Each atom in the normal state is neutral electrically. It has the same number of positive charged particles (protons) in its nucleus and the same number of negative particles (electrons) in its shells orbiting around the nucleus. If you add electrons to the atom, you have more negative particles than positive electrons. The atom in this ionic state is negatively charged. The strength of this negative depends on the number of electrons added.

The other side of the coin is if you take away negative particles then the atom (ion) becomes more positive (depending upon how many you take away).

DIRECT CURRENT

In order to accomplish the reduction of metal ions out of our bath (ion soup), you need an outside source of direct current. If you attempted to plate with alternating current, the polarity of the cathode and anode would reverse back and forth. What metal that is deposited when the cathode is negative would be removed when the cathode became positive and the anode became negative.

Chapter 6

Preparations

Before you get down to actually plating, let's talk about preparing the work. Prior to plating, the work to be plated must be clean and free of oxidation, oil, dirt, grease, and old plating. Any item to be plated, if the plating is to be a bright plate, must be highly polished. The plating can be no brighter than the surface to which it is applied.

The terms polishing and buffing are often misunderstood. Polishing refers to the actual grinding down of a surface prior to buffing it to a bright finish. The success of the buffing depends entirely on the polishing treatment prior to the buffing or rouging. It cannot be accomplished with one step unless the object is already polished out to begin with. Polishing consists of taking the object down on sanding belts, wheels headed with carborundum, or for abrasive compounds applied to a cloth buff.

Lee compounds are sold in sticks of various grits. These sticks contain an abrasive mixed with an adhesive. They are applied to the revolving buff and the sewed buff turned off while holding the stick against it, letting the stick bring the wheel to a stop. You now have a coat of adhesive and abrasive on the buff.

The wheel is allowed to air dry until the abrasive has set and is no longer tacky. The abrasive is now firmly glued to the face of the buff. Because these compounds air dry once you have opened the end of the stick to use it, when not in use cover it up with a plastic bag to keep it moist for the next application. There are a wide variety of flap wheels and belt sanders that can be used.

You can use what is known as headed wheels. These you make up yourself. They have a much longer life than compounds, belts, or whatever. They are simple and easy to produce, and in the long run pay off in better work at a lower cost.

The steps are simple and consist of gluing carborundum powder to the face of a sewn cloth buffing wheel. Buy sewn muslin cloth buffs, flake hyde glue, and several grades of carborundum (silicon carbide)—course, medium, and fine. The flake glue is put into the top of a double boiler. Just enough water is added to cover the glue and then let it stand overnight.

The soaked glue is then heated in the double boiler until it is nice and creamy. The hot glue is applied to the face of the buff with a brush, working it well into the face. The desired grit is placed in a long, narrow cardboard trough. A nail is used as an axle and the tacky buff is rolled back and forth through the abrasive grain, the excess is knocked off, and the wheel is hung to dry.

When dry it can be put to use or glued up and charged again. Building it up with several charges of abrasive will greatly increase the life of the wheel. My preference is to use two coats. When a newly charged wheel is ready to use, strike the surface with the edge of a heavy file to break or crack the surface, working your way all the way around the wheel. This gives the wheel more surface flexability. It will do a better job and last longer. See Fig. 6-1.

Progressively work down the surface by polishing it with an abrasive, moving from the courser grades to the finer grades, while working first in one direction and then the other, cross latching. See Fig. 6-2.

When the piece is down to an even satin finish, it is cleaned and then buffed to a high polish (mirror) with rouge. Plating will not fill in roughness and the final appearance. Brightness (of the plating) depends upon the condition of the piece being placed.

The success of the plating depends 90 percent upon the careful preparation and cleanliness of the piece prior to polishing with rouges, red, white, yellow, etc., for the super finishing with a minimum of work. After you get the piece down to a satin finish, before you color buff, go over the piece with what is known as bobbing compound. This is a grease stick with an abrasive that cuts very well, but leaves the surface in much better condition that the satin finish left by polishing wheels. My preference is to go from the polishing wheel to the bobbing wheel (on a cloth buff) to white or red rouge on a loose-lead center buff. I would start out with a double-

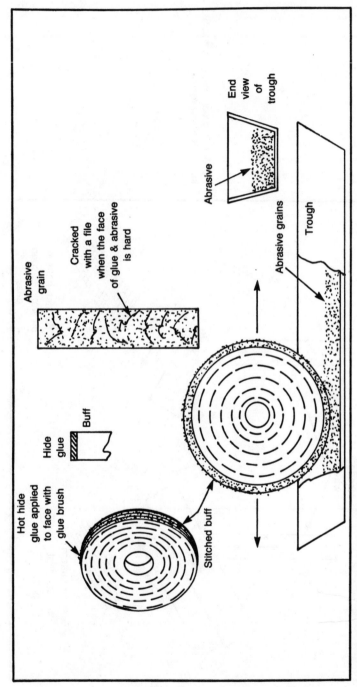

Fig. 6-1. Method of heading up a sewed buff.

Abrasive grain

Cracked with a file when the face of glue & abrasive is hard

Hide glue

Buff

Hot hide glue applied to face with glue brush

Stitched buff

End view of trough

Abrasive

Abrasive grains

Trough

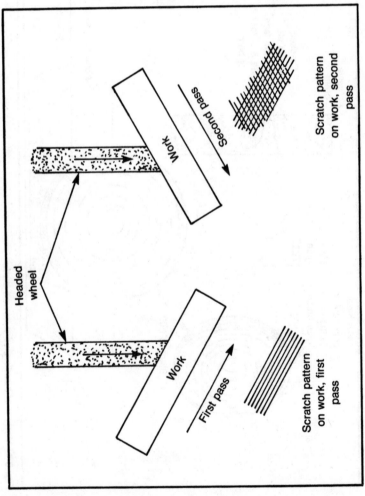

Fig. 6-2. Direction change in polishing to give best results.

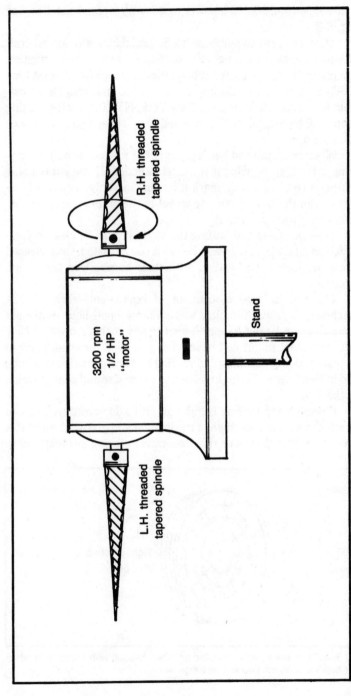

Fig. 6-3. Polishing (motor) lathe fitted with a left-hand and a right-hand tapered spindle for sewed buffs and lead center loose buffs.

73

shaft, 3200-rpm, 1/2-horsepower motor with tapered spindles. See Fig. 6-3.

Of course you can purchase buffing machines with forced-draft filters in a wide price range. For buffing rouges, wheels, spindles, and plating supplies, start out by getting catalogs from Swest Inc., 10803 Composite Dr., Dallas, Texas 75220, and from Paul Gesswein Inc., 235A Park Ave. S., New York, NY 10003. Most plating shops will be helpful with advice and they will sell you rouge, Lee compound, etc.

When polishing and buffing, never use a wheel or buff for anything other than for what it was first intended. If you put bobbing compound on a new buff, mark it for that use only. You should always clean the work from one wheel to the other to prevent contaminating the next wheel.

After polishing and buffing the work, it must be cleaned completely of all rouge and grease, before it can be plated. Once cleaned it can no longer be handled with your hands. Use hooks and tweezers.

There is a large assortment of equipment—abrasive belt machines, abrasive tumbler, and vibratory polishing units—out there that can be put to use. A visit to any rock shop where they sell equipment might just have what you need for small parts to be plated. Doing polishing and buffing by hand can drive you nuts, and in some cases it is impossible due to the size and configuration of the item.

Polishing and buffing is quite an art to do correctly. You can wreck the item at this stage of the game if you groove the surface, destroy surface details or ruin decorative etching or create sharp

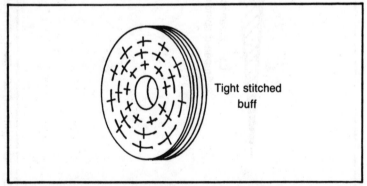

Tight stitched buff

Fig. 6-4. Tight sewed buff for polishing when headed with abrasive or when not headed used for bobbing or rouge wheel.

74

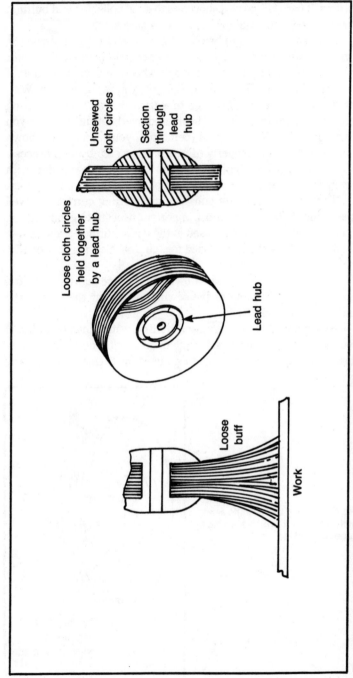

Loose cloth circles
held together
by a lead hub

Unsewed
cloth circles

Section
through
lead
hub

Lead hub

Loose
buff

Work

Fig. 6-5. Loose-lead center buff used for final high polish with red rouge only.

75

corners. There are no real shortcuts to good polishing and buffing. You will get into trouble if you try to skip steps.

Let's say the item to be plated is a sand casting, and you are trying for a mirror-finish, bright silver or gold plating. You don't try to polish it out with a single grit wheel; this will not do it. If you start out with a fine-wheel, 220 grit, you eat up wheels. With the work being relatively rough to start with, you wind up taking forever. In addition, you will score and overheat the work. If you start out with a 60-grit wheel (belt, etc.), you cannot get it down fine enough to buff properly (if at all). It's a step-by-step process. When you sand down a piece of rough wood, you should start with a very course paper, then a medium paper, and then a fine paper.

The time spent doing polishing and buffing correctly is well spent, and its one of the most important aspects to good plating. Concentric-sewed buffs are used in the initial buffing. See Fig. 6-4. Lead center loose buffs are used for the final high polish. See Fig. 6-5.

When a sewed buff wears down and the face gets too tight and hard, you can cut some of the sewing loose near the face of the buff. See Fig. 6-6.

Never crossbreed rouges and buffing compounds on buffs. If you use a new buff with red rouge to start with, never apply anything to this buff but the rouge first used on it. Don't use bobbing

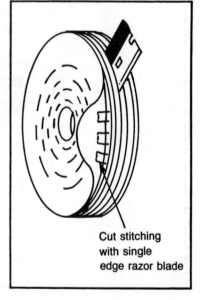

Fig. 6-6. Cutting a concentric sewed buff to loosen it up. Use a single-edge razor blade.

Cut stitching with single edge razor blade

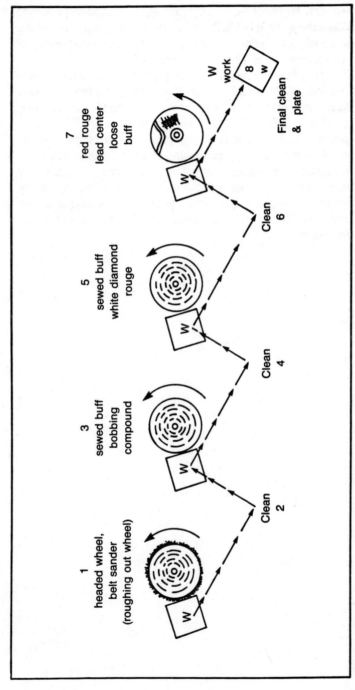

Fig. 6-7. Proper sequence of polishing and buffing and do a real job and not contaminate your wheels.

on this buff. Have a separate buff for each compound or rouge.

When the work is bobbed, you must clean the work free of the bobbing compound before moving to another wheel in order to prevent contamination of wheels. See Fig. 6-7.

Polishing is where you make or break it. There are no short-cuts to good polishing and buffing. You must spend the time here.

Ninety percent of the time spent in successful plating is preparing the item to be plated and 10 percent is spent in doing the actual plating. You don't have to bog yourself down with all kinds of rouges. A good bobbing compound and a red rouge will cover 99 percent of your buffing. For your abrasive grits, whether they be headed wheels or belts, you need only a few grits such as 60, 100, and 200. After 200-grit work, the bobbing compound will go fast and easy. Then a good red rouge will give you the mirror finish you require.

Chapter 7

Cleaning

Even the film from your hands will soil the item and prevent the affected area from plating, even if it does plate, the plating will soon peel off the soiled area. The greatest cause of peeling is that the work is not clean to start out. There is an old saying in the plating shops "When it is clean, clean it again."

If the work is not clean, three things will happen:

- ☐ The piece will refuse to plate.
- ☐ The plating will be patchy or spotty.
- ☐ The plating will peel.

This usually happens when you are finished and very pleased with yourself. The piece to be plated must be clinically clean. When cleaning, you must work up a system and make it a ritual. Working a system into a ritual will prove not to be an unpleasant chore. The results obtained and the absence of disappointments will make it pleasant.

Animal fats and vegetable fats are what we call the greases. Lubricating oils and cup grease are what we call mineral greases. There is a decided difference and they must be removed by different means. If you try to remove lube oil (a mineral oil) with caustic soda (lye) or soap, which is a product of the action of a caustic solution on animal or vegetable fat, you will soon realize that it's not going to work. Mineral oil must be removed by a solvent such as benzine or carbon tetrachloride. Benzene is really inflammable while carbon tet. is not.

To reap the full benefit of both products without the fire hazard of benzene, mix the two half and half and you wind up with a very good noninflammable cleaning liquid. The work is cleaned first by using the benzene and carbon tet. 50/50 (by volume) mix. A very light film of grease will be left on the work after this cleaner evaporates. This is easily removed with the next step (caustic cleaner).

If you were completely sure that the object contained no mineral oil or grease, you could skip the solvent step. There is no way of being really sure. In the long run it pays to give everything a solvent cleaning. Avoid breathing the fumes and work in a well-ventilated area. Small pieces can be scrubbed with solvent cleaner and a toothbrush. Wear rubber gloves because the solvent can play havic with your skin. Some of us are allergic to these solutions.

With the mineral grease removed, now tackle the animal and vegetable fats. Use just a plain old hot-soap-suds solution to which we have added a pinch or two of sodium carbonate (washing soda).

Another good solution is a pound of lye (sodium hydroxide) to 2 1/2 gallons of water. Use this one hot. Remember that lye is very caustic and can cause severe skin burns. Keep away from children and wear rubber gloves and an eye shield when messing with this. Aluminum is highly soluble in lye, and the reaction is quite violent when aluminum, lye and water come together. The common household products are simply dry lye and little chips of aluminum. It is the reaction of the aluminum, lye and water that causes the heat and gas pressure to open up your drain. So never, never put anything caustic in an aluminum pot. Use steel enameled ware or cast iron.

Another good caustic cleaning solution that has a slight abrasive action is 2 ounces of lye (sodium hydroxide), 10 ounces washing soda, 2 ounces trisodium phosphate, 1 ounce sodium silicate, and 1 gallon of water.

You can add to this solution 2 ounces of sodium cyanide. This will remove stains (patina) from previous solutions. Remember that if you add the 2 ounces of cyanide, you must use the precautions observed with any and all cyanide solutions. They are very poisonous. My preference is not to add the cyanide but to remove any stains with an acid pickle solution. When cleaning any item of tin, zinc, or aluminum with a caustic solution, you must work fast and rinse the work well after removing it from the solution (these metals are dissolved by sodium hydroxide). To avoid etching move quickly.

ELECTRO CLEANING

Here you can use either of the above caustic solutions for a piece of stainless steel. With the caustic solution as the electrolite, we pass current through this setup. A copious evolution of hydrogen gas will do the cleaning by the mechanical action of the bubbles and the chemical action of the solution. The best method is to use a stainless steel container and make this your + or anode connection and the work or cathode connection. See Fig. 7-1. Use full voltage with a hot solution and clean the work for a maximum of about three minutes. Then reverse the current for not over five seconds maximum. This makes the work the anode, momentarily, removing the hydrogen bubbles. Any longer and a reverse polarity will cause the work to build up an oxide surface. Then you are back to polishing. The simplest setup is to have a polarity reversing switch between your power source and your work and tank. See Fig. 7-2.

You can make up several special electro cleaning solutions if you like. They have some advantages but, if your electro cleaning solution is doing a good job, why bother. See Table 7-1.

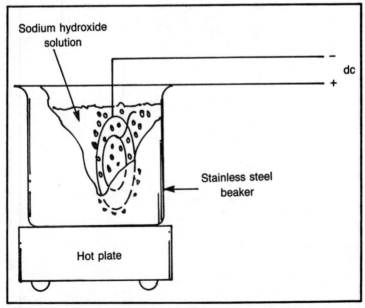

Fig. 7-1. Set up for electro cleaning small items with sodium hydroxide.

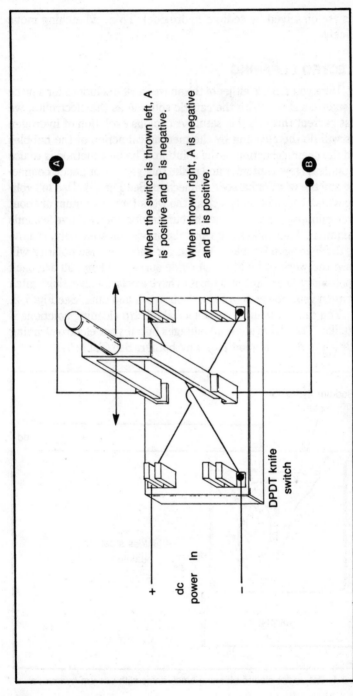

When the switch is thrown left, A is positive and B is negative.

When thrown right, A is negative and B is positive.

DPDT knife switch

dc power In

+

−

Fig. 7-2. Polarity-reversing, switch double-pole, double-throw switch wiring diagram.

Table 7-1. Cleaning Solutions.

Iron & Steel	
Lye	8 oz.
Laundry soap	2 oz.
Water	1 gal.
Copper & Brass	
Lye	1 oz.
Washing soda	5 oz.
Trisodium phosphate	2 oz.
Laundry soap	1 oz.
Water	1 gal.
Aluminum, Zinc & Tin	
Sodium bicarbonate	4 oz.
Washing soda	4 oz.
Water	1 gal.

Some hobbyists like to use a combination electro cleaning and coppering bath. One that works very well consists of:

Lye (caustic soda), 8 ounces.
  Sodium cyanide, 6 ounces.
  Copper cyanide, 4 ounces.
  Sodium carbonate, 6 ounces.
  Distilled water, 1 gallon.

As you see from the preceeding, you have a poisoness cyanide solution. Treat it as such; don't relax your precautions. Make the work full voltage, 6 volts, lower the work into the solution. As it cleans, you will note the work will become covered with a thin coat of copper. When it is completely covered, remove it, then rinse it in hot water and then cold running water. Then it should go directly into your copper plating bath. There is no need for the 5-second, current-reversing step when using the above combination (clean and plate). The thin plate from the above is called a strike plate, and it only prepares the object for the actual build-up plate from a regular bath.

PICKLES AND PICKLING

Because chemical tarnish (patina) on the surface of an item to be plated does not make a good base for plating, it must be removed with what is known as a pickle solution. After the work has been thoroughly cleaned and free from grease and oils, and upon examination it is splotched with patina (colors), it must be pickled to remove these oxide films.

These solutions are acid solutions for the most part and the work is simply dipped into them for a short period to dissolve the patina. Because the pickle solution attacks the object if left in the pickle too long, the surface will become pitted and badly etched. After the pickle, the object must be rinsed in hot and cold running water to make certain that no acid is left in the metal pores. Otherwise you will spoil the plating.

The best containers for pickles are ceramic crocks that have a heavy glaze inside and out. You must always, when making a mixture of acid and water, add the acid slowly to the water—**never** water to acid. When you add water to acid, a violent reaction and spitting takes place that could cause great harm. When you mix acid to water, heat is generated. If you add the acid too rapidly to the water or too much at a time, the heat buildup could be too fast and too hot, and it could crack the container. Add acid slowly, allow for the solution to cool, and then add more acid. Repeat until the desired percent of acid to water is reached.

Warning. Acids and cyanides, when they come together, produce deadly cyanide gas. *Take great precaution. Never let this happen.* I keep all acids on one end of the room and cyanides on the other end. After pickling the work, it is thoroughly washed in running hot and cold water before entering a cyanide plating bath.

More On Pickling

Not only is pickling a very important operation in plating, but you will find that there is a wide variety of items that require pickling. Perhaps someone brings you a brass or copper item that is covered with a patina they want removed and the item simply polished. Or perhaps you polish a silver piece and after degreasing, you find it has some discolored blotches that will not polish out. See Fig. 7-3.

The discoloration is often called a blush. It is caused by getting an isolated area too hot while buffing (not keeping the piece moving). Of course it stands to reason if you hold the piece in one spot on the buff with too much pressure you are going to do one or two things for sure:

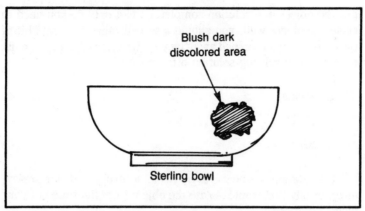

Fig. 7-3. Heat blush on caused by overheating with the buff.

☐ Polish a flat spot on the piece.
☐ Cause a heat blush.

In the case of sterling silver, the blush is caused by copper crystals that have migrated to the surface.

If the piece is dipped in a very well diluted nitric acid solution, (1 part nitric to 6 parts water heated to 80 degrees Fahrenheit), the blush (copper) on its surface will be removed. The piece is then washed with lots of water, to neutralize the acid, and lightly buffed with a little fine rouge on a loose buff.

You might have an aluminum item that is badly coated with aluminum oxide (white to grayish patina) you want to remove in order to restore the object's beauty. You need a pickle for aluminum.

The key word for pickling is the removing of various metal oxides from the surface of the item. What you are doing is dissolving the unwanted oxide with an acid or basic solution. With a rusty piece of steel, the rust is iron oxide. If iron oxide is soluble in an acid, then by dipping the rusty object in the correct acid solution the rust will dissolve into the solution, leaving the surface of the object free of the rust.

Problems With Pickling

Pickling is a process where you have to be on your toes. Once the oxides are removed, you must remove the object quickly and rinse because the solution will keep eating away and pit the surface of the object. If left in the pickle long enough, pickling will put the object into solution completely. Not only do you need to rinse the object well, you should also neutralize any little bit of pickle solution not carried away by your first rinse. Then you must rinse the neutralizing solution off:

- ☐ Pickle.
- ☐ Rinse.
- ☐ Neutralize.
- ☐ Rinse.

Like plating, it's no use to try to pickle an object that is greasy, dirty, or oily that would isolate the object from the action of your pickle solution.

Let's pickle a rusty nail. Clean the nail in a hot lye solution to remove any grease, and then rinse it in water. Now dip it in a solution of 1 part sulfuric acid and 15 parts of water heated 140 degrees Fahrenheit. In an instant, the rust is dissolved in the pickle solution.

Rinse the nail. Because the pickle is an acid, you must make sure the acid is completely removed. An acid is neutralized with a basic solution (alkali). If you rinse the nail in a dilute sodium hydroxide solution, you would kill the acid. Now rerinse with water and dry. After drying, you can coat the nail with a protective coating of some sort to prevent it from rusting again. In the case of a brass, copper, or bronze item, you could coat it with a clear laquer.

If you left the nail in the sulfuric acid solution until it is completely dissolved and then evaporated the solution, you would wind up with crystals if iron sulfate $FeSO_4 \cdot 7 H_2O$, also called Green Vitrol or *copperas*.

Don't confuse the word copperas with any copper compound. The iron sulfate is a water-soluble, pale-green crystalline salt used in ironplating, dying, tanning, ink manufacturing, and to precipitate gold.

What's Soluble In What? Aluminum and aluminum oxide (alumina) are highly soluble in a basic solution. (Our nail is not soluble in a basic solution.) We would use sodium hydroxide, a base to pickle or etch aluminum, and a mild acid solution to neutralize the base, and then rinse.

BRIGHT DIPS

Let's clear the air about pickles and bright dips. They both do the same thing, but the pickle is much more aggressive and is considered as a method to remove a scale. Let's look at a formula for a pickle for gold and a bright dip for gold.

Gold is an example where you pickle in an acid solution. The gold is not soluble but the heat scale on it is soluble. Then bright dip in a solution in which gold is soluble.

A jeweler or goldsmith will weld members of gold together (usually karat gold) in order to produce the desired item (a ring, etc.). In this process, the goldsmith usually dips the component parts in a solution of alcohol and boric acid, and then ignites the alcohol.

The alcohol burns off and leaves the individual components covered with a thin film of boric acid. This treatment is to minimize the formation of fire scale when hard soldering the pieces together. In most cases, you wind up with some fire scale anyway. The assembled piece is then pickled to remove the fire scale. This is usually done in a copper pickle pan. See Fig. 7-4.

The piece is heated for a few minutes in a pickle solution consisting of 1 part sulfuric acid and 5 parts water. This removes the fire scale and any flux used in the hard soldering operation. The pickle is poured into a crock and the pickle pan with the object in it is rinsed under the faucet.

The piece is now polished on the polishing lathe and placed in a boil-out pot. The solution in the boil-out pot is simply water, liquid detergent, and a spot of ammonia (Ammonium hydroxide).

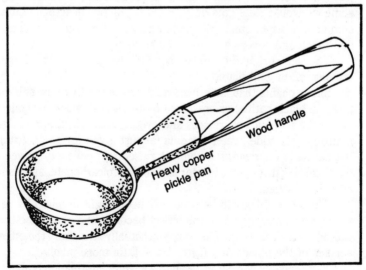

Fig. 7-4. Jeweler's heavy copper pickle pan.

The item or items are placed in a strainer so that they can be jiggled around and the solution brought to a boil.

Usually it only takes a few minutes to remove the polishing rouge from the items, which are then rinsed under the tap. See Fig. 7-5.

From here on you do not touch the item or items with your hands. Use copper or stainless wire hooks. The next step is the bright dip. The pieces immersed in the following solution at room temperature: 3 ounces of sodium cyanide NaCN dissolved in 1 gallon of distilled water, to which you add 4 ounces of hydrogen peroxide (H_2O_2).

Gold is soluble in sodium cyanide to which an oxidizer is added (hydrogen peroxide). You actually strip off a very very thin layer of gold from the item being bright dipped. It goes into solution as gold ions (cations). See Fig. 7-6.

The dissolving away of a thin outer layer of metal leaves the item bright and clean. The usual procedure for a bright dip using cyanide and hydrogen peroxide is to make up a gallon of cyanide solution, just pour enough as needed into a beaker, and add the hydrogen peroxide needed for the amount of cyanide solution you are going to use. The solution decomposes rather rapidly when you add the hydrogen peroxide. Each time you bright dip you need a fresh solution of water NaCN and H_2O_2.

The object is rinsed using copious amounts of water. The object is not ready for plating or left as is. You might wonder why someone would plate gold on gold. This practice is actually quite common. A bright quick gold plate on a gold item gives it that added touch and covers any off color at solder joints.

The same bright dip can be used for silver items. Silver items are also often gold plated.

Silver chains that have become tarnished with silver sulfate (gray to black patina) are restored quite easily if they are boiled out in the boil-out pot, rinsed, and bright dipped in the cyanide, hydrogen peroxide, water formula (as just given for gold). After the patina is removed, the chain is rinsed and polished between the fingers with a paste of water and sodium bicarbonate, and then rinsed and dried.

The same thing can be accomplished (bright dipping) by reverse electroplating where the object becomes the anode and the cathode is the container. This way you actually strip away the other surface of the object. It's faster but a little more involved.

You probably wonder what all this jewelry information is about.

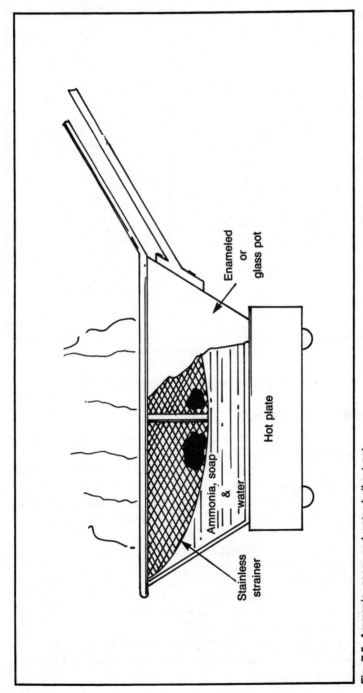

Fig. 7-5. Ammonia, soap, and water boil-out pot.

Enameled
or
glass pot

Hot plate

Ammonia, soap
&
water

Stainless
strainer

89

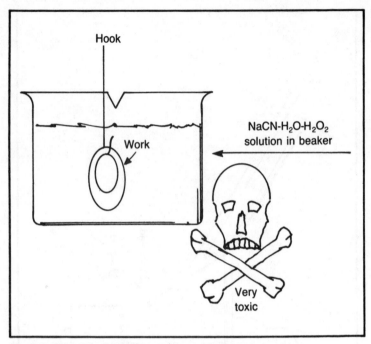

Fig. 7-6. Bright dipping with cyanide and hydrogen peroxide.

It's all relative. Jewelers do a great deal of plating.

BRIGHT STRIPPING

The object to be stripped is made the anode and the container the cathode. See Fig. 7-7.

The item to be bright stripped is first pickled in the sulfuric-acid, water-pickle solution and rinsed completely free from acid. Remember cyanide and acid *do not* mix. Remember your cyanide rules. The stripping solution consists of the following:

Potassium cyanide (KCN) 4 ounces.

Potassium ferrocyanide ($K_4Fe(CN)_6 3H_2O$) – , 2 ounces.

Distilled water, 1 gallon.

The container is made the cathode (–) and the object the anode (+). The solution is heated to 150 degrees Fahrenheit and the voltage is set at 10 to 12 volts. It only takes a few seconds to produce an extremely bright, clean finish.

Potassium ferrocyanide is yellow prussiate of potash. This compound itself has a low toxicity, but if heated to a red heat it evolves highly toxic fumes.

90

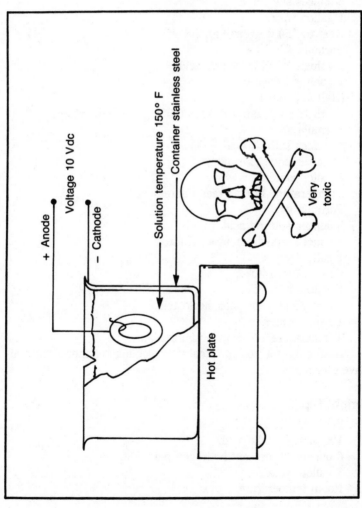

Fig. 7-7. Electro-bright strip with work at anode (solution cyanide).

Pickling and Brightening Setup

A good, safe way to do this part of the operation is to set up in a sink. The sink can be stainless steel, enameled cast iron, plastic, or lead-lined wood. See Fig. 7-8.

The following are several choices numbered 1, 2, 3, etc. Each formula is to be used as given. You do not add formula 1 to 2 or anything like that.

Pickle Iron and Steel

Formula #1.
8 ounces sulfuric acid.
1 gallon water.
Heat to 150 degrees Fahrenheit.
Formula #2.
1 volume of hydrochloric acid.
1 volume of water
(Half and Half)
Work at room temperatures (70 degrees Fahrenheit).
Formula #3.
4 ounces sulfuric acid.
4 ounces potassium nitrate.
1 gallon water.
Temperature 140 degrees Fahrenheit.
Formula #4.
6 ounces sulfuric acid.
5 ounces anhydrous iron sulfate.
1 gallon water.
Room temperature.
Formula #5.
1 pint 75 percent phosphoric acid.
1 gallon water.
Temperature 170 degrees Fahrenheit.
Bright dips for iron and steel after pickling in either of the five given formulas.

Bright Dip

Formula #1.
100 grams oxalic acid.
6 ounces 30 percent hydrogen peroxide.
1 gallon water.
Room temperature.

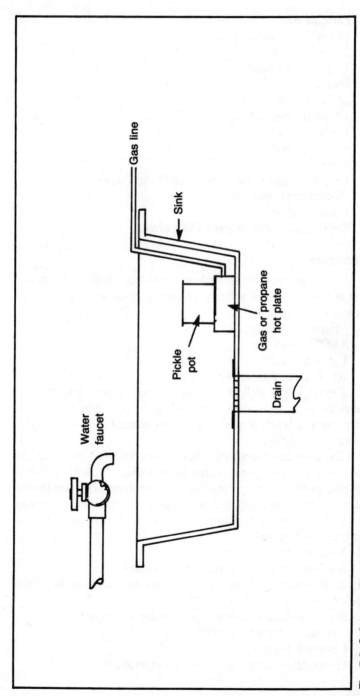

Fig. 7-8. Safe setup for pickling and bright dipping.

93

Formula #2.

15 ounces chromic acid.

1 gallon water.

Temperature boiling.

Formula #3.

10 fluid ounces nitric.

4 fluid ounces sulfuric.

1 gallon water.

Room temperature.

Formula #4.

Here is a simple, very good bright dip for steel:

15 ounces chromic acid.

1 gallon water.

Temperature 140 degrees Fahrenheit.

Aluminum

Aluminum is easily etched or frosted by dipping the clean, grease-free item in a solution of caustic soda (lye, sodium hydroxide).

Aluminum Etch:

3 to 9 ounces lye

1 gallon water

200 degrees Fahrenheit

The degree of etch or frosting depends on how long you immerse the aluminum (aluminum is soluble in lye). When the aluminum starts to react, it produces a great volume of hydrogen gas, which is explosive.

The settlement is alumina (aluminum oxide). This should be done with plenty of forced ventilation and where the hydrogen cannot find ignition from an open flame. No smoking. Because the solution is caustic (a base), you must neutralize the item by rinsing in water and then an acid bath. For an acid bath to neutralize aluminum etch bath use:

1 volume of nitric acid.

1 volume of water, at room temperature.

Dip the item in this solution for only a few seconds, and then rinse in clean hot water and then cold water.

For an aluminum bright dip for sheet aluminum use:

1 volume hydrofluoric acid.

1 volume nitric acid.

100 volumes of water, at room temperature.

About a minute in the above dip will usually do the trick. Rinse in hot water then cold water.

Let's talk about hydrofluoric acid. This acid is hydrogen fluoride absorbed in water and it is a powerful acid that will etch glass. Years ago we bought hydrofluoric acid in wax containers. Today it comes in polyethylene bottles. You must use it in polyethylene containers. It is highly corrosive to the skin and mucous membranes, and it is also highly toxic by ingestion and inhalation. Be extremely *Careful*.

For bright dip for aluminum castings use:

40 fluid ounces phosphoric acid 75 percent.

3 fluid ounces nitric acid.

3 fluid ounces acetic acid.

5 fluid ounces water, at boiling temperature.

A few seconds should do the trick. Rinse in hot then cold water.

There will be times when you are called upon to silver or copper cadmium plated objects. In this case you will have to bright dip the item and at the same time avoid stripping the cadmium from the object. The cadmium plating might be quite thin. The simplest way to go is with 1 to 1.5 fluid ounces of nitric acid in a gallon of water and work fast. This mix of nitric and water usually will pickle and bright dip all in one. The part is ready to plate after it is washed in hot water then cold water.

A Note on Water

In most cases with pickling solutions you can use tap water, but it should always be free of chlorine. The two simplest methods are to vacuum off the chlorine or bubble it off with a fish tank aerator. You can buy an inexpensive unit (for example, at the pet store) that consists of a simple air pump and a porous spurger. See Fig. 7-9.

If you get the setup as shown in A of Fig. 7-9, you can line up a dozen jugs of tap water and spurge #1 and then #2, etc., to build up a supply. It takes usually about 20 minutes to spurge off the chlorine in 1 gallon of water, and about 5 minutes with a vacuum pump.

The nose is usually very sensitive to the odor of chlorine. You first smell the water in the jug and then chlorine is all gone or at a level that will not affect your formula. You can buy, from a swimming pool product supplier, a chlorine testing kit that is very sim-

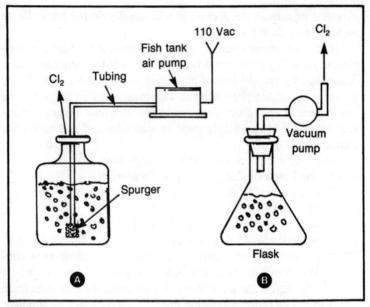

Fig. 7-9. Two methods for removing chlorine from tap water.

ple to use and will give you the Cl_2 in parts per million. This way you can test the water before and after spurging.

In all cases with plating solutions, use distilled water. Most tap water contains various elements of sodium, iron, copper, etc., that will affect your plating solution. If you put your water in a shallow container that gives the water a relatively large surface area—and simply let it sit for 24 hours, usually the chlorine will have gassed off.

Pickle for Copper

Any copper or copper-base items that contain 85 percent copper and the remaining 15 percent other alloys lead, zinc, tin etc., if not heavily coated with patina (Cu_2O) cuprious oxide, can be pickled with a simple sulfuric acid water pickle consisting of:

1 part sulfuric acid.

5 parts water, boiling or near boiling, preferably in a copper pickle pan.

If the piece is badly patinaed with a heavy Cu_2O covering, it will be difficult to remove it with sulfuric alone. Then you must add an oxidizing agent such as sodium dichromate $Na_2Cr_2O_7 \cdot 2\ H_2O$. Here you have lots of oxygen to do the trick. Another good oxidizing agent, Oxone, is made by Dupont. Oxone is a very powerful oxidizing agent (a triple salt) $2KHSO_5 \cdot KHSO_4 \cdot K_2SO_4$. When either sodium dichromate or oxone decompose, they release oxygen (that does the trick).

When pickling copper and copper alloys, you have a problem. If you want to pickle a yellow brass item that consists of 70 percent copper 30 percent zinc, copper is much more readily soluble in nitric acid than zinc, and zinc is more soluble in hydrochloric than copper. Therefore, if the pickle is high in nitric acid than zinc, and zinc is more soluble in hydrochloric than copper. Therefore, if the pickle is high in nitric acid it will dissolve the copper from the surface of the item—leaving it with a white discoloration of undissolved zinc. To combat this problem use two pickle solutions. These are exactly the same; only the ratio between the acids differ.

The first dip is a pickle to remove patina and the second dip is to restore the surface to its original bright color. This dip is therefore called a bright dip.

The object is first pickled in the following dip: Slowly add 70 ounces of sulfuric acid to 2 quarts of water (when doing this stir continuously with a glass rod to keep the fuss down and aid in cooling). When this solution is cool, slowly add 14 ounces of nitric acid and 1 ounce of hydrochloric acid. Rinse the work and the bright dip.,

The bright dip uses 70 ounces of sulfuric acid to 2 quarts water. When cool, add 11 ounces of nitric acid, 1/3 ounce hydrochloric acid and 3 ounces of lamp black.

Still another formula would be 1 pint sulfuric acid and 1 gallon of water. To the above solution, you can add 5 or 6 ounces of sodium dichromate or about an ounce or two of a saturated Oxone solution (which is 25 grams dissolved in about a cup of water). You can use this pickle at room temperature or up to about 150 °F.

Scaling Dip

Scaling dip is sometimes used after pickling and prior to a bright dip. The action of a scaling dip is to smooth out the surface and it results in a nice, uniform clean finish when the work comes from the bright dip. Scaling dip:

1 gal. of sulfuric acid.

1/2 gal. of nitric acid.

3 gal. water, at room temperature. Keep the work moving (agitated). If the action is too violent, you can add additional sulfuric acid to calm it down.

Bright Dip for Copper

From the pickle bath or the scaling dip, the item is bright dipped in the following: Copper bright dip:

1 gallon of sulfuric acid.
1/2 gallon of nitric acid.
1 gallon of water.
1 teaspoon salt NaCl (table salt).

Note. With all pickles, strips, and bright dips, you must also rinse between dips. Running hot and cold water is the best but you can use plastic containers. With containers, however, you have some drag out that is carried across. When this is an excess, it eventually can be carried over into your plating bath and give you problems. Another problem is that, if you acid pickle and rinse in a bucket prior to going into a cyanide bath, soon the water in the wash bucket becomes acidic and you start dragging acid into the cyanide bath. This not only destroys the cyanide but you produce the deadly HCN gas. See Fig. 7-10.

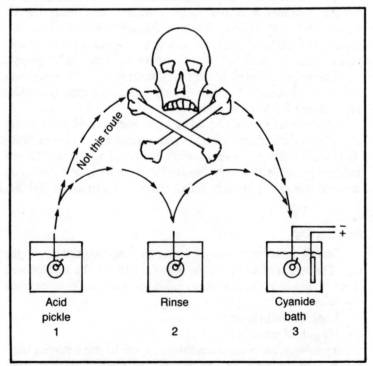

Fig. 7-10. A must when going from an acid pickle or bright dip then into a cyanide plating bath.

Play it safe. Pickle, wash under hot and then cold running water. Bright dip, wash under hot and cold running water, and then plate. After plating, rinse under hot running water then cold later. The exception to the rule is when plating with precious metals such as gold and silver. In such cases, you usually are plating in a cyanide solution so you must be positive that you do not drag over any acid into the bath.

When the item has been plated, the solution clinging to the item (when it is lifted from the plating bath) contains precious metal ions. These you do not want to wash down the drain with running water. At this point, you rinse them off in a clean plastic bucket of distilled water. Then rinse in hot and cold running water. This first rinse from the plating bath into the distilled water bucket is used as water in making up new solutions and to add to your plating baths to make up for evaporation. See Fig. 7-11.

Gold pickle:
1 part sulfuric acid.
7 parts water.
Heat in copper pickle pot, used to remove fire scale.
Gold bright dip:
5 ounces of sodium cyanide.
1 gallon of water (distilled), at room temperature.

The cyanide solution is made up as a stock solution. To bright dip, place enough of the cyanide/water solution in a beaker to cover the gold items by about one-quarter of an inch. Now add a dash of 30 percent hydrogen peroxide. This solution must be made up fresh for each application. We used to call this solution bombing. It is a fast, bright dip for gold nuggets and jewelry.

Strip or scaling dip for gold:
6 ounces potassium cyanide.
1 gallon distilled water.
4 ounces Rochelle salt.
The above solution is heated in a stainless steel container. The container is made the cathode and the article is made the anode. The voltage is 12 volts. It only takes a few seconds to do the job. See Fig. 7-12.

Another solution which works as well this way is:
4 ounces potassium cyanide.
2 ounces potassium ferra cyanide.
1 gallon distilled water.
150°F 12 V. reverse plate.

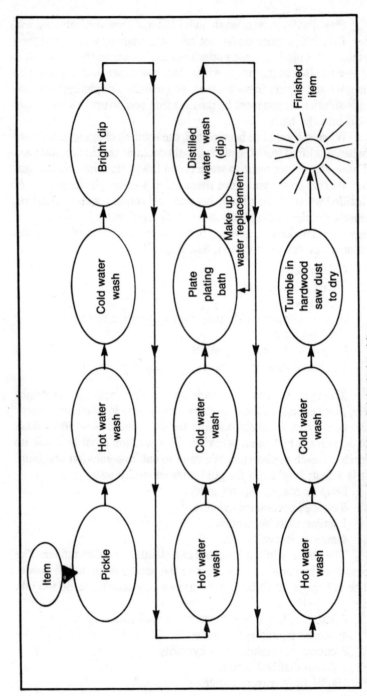

Fig. 7-11. Flow sheet for correct plating from pickle to finished plated item.

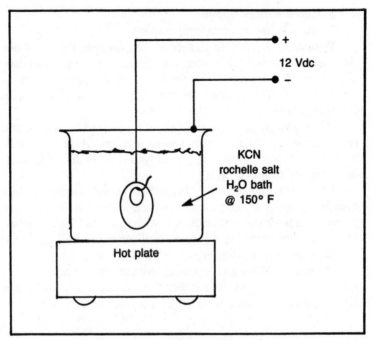

Fig. 7-12. Potassium cyanide rochelle salt electro strip.

Note. Rochelle salt is potassium (sodium-tartrate). This common, general-purpose food additive is used in baking powders, medicine (cathartic) and (widely) in plating solutions. It is also called tartaric acid.

Scaling dip for nickel alloys:

1/2 gallon hydrochloric acid.

1/4 pound cupric chloride.

1 gallon water, at 150 degrees Fahrenheit; Wash in hot water, then cold.

Silver is soluble in dilute nitric acid. You have to watch that you don't leave it in your sealing dip too long.

Scaling Dip for Silver:

1 part nitric acid.

1 part distilled water, at room temperature for slow action and 140 degrees Fahrenheit for quick action. Rinse in hot then cold water.

The dip given for gold brightening will also work well with silver. Use as you would with gold. See gold bright dip.

Bright dip for zinc:

20 ounces chromic acid.

3 ounces sodium sulfate.

1 gallon water at room temperature.

With zinc, about 30 to 40 seconds usually does the job. After rinsing with hot and cold water, sometimes you will get a surface discoloring that appears as brassy film. If this happens, it can be removed by dipping it in a 15-percent chromic-acid solution until it dissappears.

When you strip, clean, or bright dip in an acid solution, you must neutralize the acid with a base solution. (Acid treatment: Pickle, etc., wash in hot water, cold water, neutralize acid wash in hot water then cold water.)

You can neutralize the acid in any base solution such as sodium bicarb solution or a dilute sodium hydroxide solution. The reverse is true for a basic solution such as an etch in sodium hydroxide solution for aluminum. Here your neutralizer would be a mild acid solution, nitric acid, vinegar water, etc.

Warning. Although cyanide solutions are basic, you don't neutralize them with acid. Remember this produces the deadly gas HCN hydrogen cyanide used in the gas chamber.

NEUTRALIZATION OF CYANIDE SOLUTIONS

What do you do with foul or spent cyanide plating solutions and cyanide strips and brighteners? Disposal of toxic wastes is a problem. You can't simply wash them down the drain or toilet. Refer to the P-trap danger described in Chapter 3.

Cyanide solutions can be destroyed a number of ways. As I have already stated, a base is neutralized by an acid and an acid by a base. Sodium cyanide or potassium cyanide KCN are very basic, but to destroy either with an acid you produce HCN (which is deadly). So you will have to take a different track. Chloride readily decomposes KCN or NaCN and this is the way to go. Let's take an example.

Let's say you have a cyanide solution from plating or stripping that might be carrying precious metals in the form of silver or gold cations in sufficient quality to save and reuse or sell. Your first move would be to reduce the values to metallics. In order to do this you must first remove any oxygen present because the metal ions are complexed with the cyanide and oxygen. Gold, silver, copper are not soluble in cyanide without the presence of free oxygen (an oxidizer). This is why you add hydrogen peroxide to your cyanide strip and bright dips.

In order to remove the free oxygen we can go two ways. Vacuum it out or simply let it sit around in glass baking pans to give us lots of surface area. See Fig. 7-13.

You can accomplish this oxygen spurge with a vacuum pump in 20 minutes or less. If you let it do its own thing, it can take from 24 hours to several days.

When the ion-carrying cyanide solution is free of free oxygen, you simply hang a chunk of zinc metal in the solution and the zinc will go into solution by ion exchange and swap places with the precious metals. This reduces them from an oxidized condition to metallics, which will settle to the bottom of your container as a mud. See Fig. 7-14.

If the values you have reduced from the solution are mostly gold, the mud will be brown to black. If mostly silver, it will be a gray color similar to cement (it is actually called cement silver).

The mud is filtered off on to a filter paper and washed with several volumes of water to free it of any residual cyanide. See Fig. 7-15. The filter paper, with the mud, is allowed to dry and the mud is sold to refiner or parted and used as make up metal for plating.

Now to the cyanide solution left over from our zinc extraction. Place this solution in a large beaker or Erlemeyer flask, and add to this solution a pinch of sodium hypochlorite Na OC1. $5H_2O$. Watch for bubbles. When the solution stops bubbling, add another pinch, and watch for bubbles. When the cyanide solution quits bubbling (reacting), you have destroyed the cyanide. At this point add a little more sodium hypochlorite. Let the solution set overnight and go to waste with lots of water. This operation is done at room temperature.

Sodium hypochlorite is a very strong oxidizing agent that is soluble in water but is destroyed in hot water. It is used in the manufacture of bleaches, to chlorinate swimming pools, and as a chemical reagent. You can buy it from any swimming pool supplier as a solution or as a powder or tablet.

Another way to deal with cyanide is by bubbling chlorine Cl_2 gas through the solution until it is destroyed. This system takes special equipment, venting, and lung-protection equipment. This work should not be attempted by a novice.

With sodium hypochlorite as an oxidizer of cyanide, you should make sure that the pH of the solution you want to destroy is above 8. You can adjust your solution to about pH 10 with sodium hydroxide (lye), using pH papers to check. Then go with your sodium hypochlorite. The pH value is defined as the hydrogen ion concen-

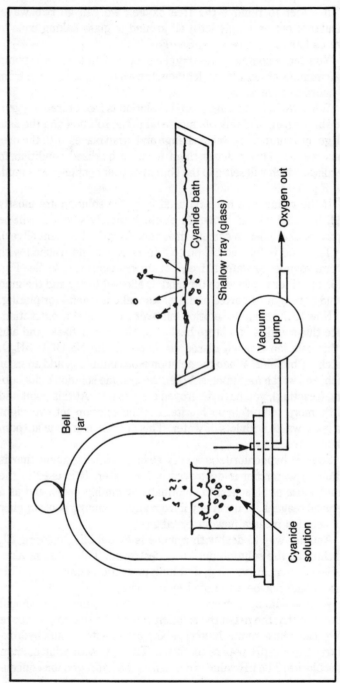

Fig. 7-13. Removing free oxygen from spent cyanide baths or stripping baths in order to recover precious metals in the solution by ion exchange with zinc.

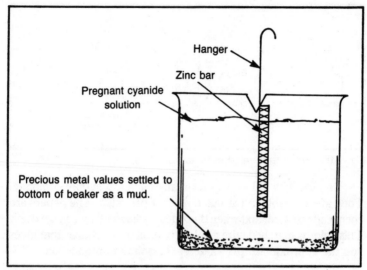

Fig. 7-14. Dropping precious metal valves out of a deoxidized pregnant cyanide solution with metallic zinc.

tration or the number of grams of hydrogen ions per liter of solution.

What you will be concerned with is how acid or how basic a solution is without all the chemistry involved, working in a range from 0 to 14 pH. See Fig. 7-16.

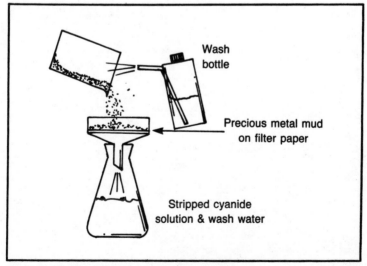

Fig. 7-15. Filtering off and washing precious metal valves recovered from ion exchange (Fig. 7-14).

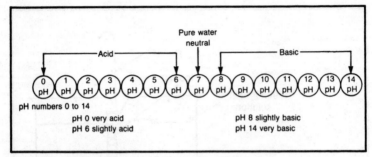

Fig. 7-16. Acid or base relationship to pH valves.

You can buy pH papers from any chemical supply company. They are available in various ranges of pH value. The papers are chemically treated, and when dipped in a solution they change color. This color is matched with a color chart on the container that gives you the approximate pH value of the solution in question.

Chapter 8

Stripping Old Plating

When replating an object that is worn or scratched or has a portion of the plating flaked off, to simply clean up the item and go on top with a new coat of plating usually results in a botched job. You have the problem of color matching. If you plate an object where the plating has flaked off, you cannot fill in the missing area and level things out. See Fig. 8-1.

You do have a somewhat better chance if the plating that's missing is simply worn off down to the base metal on a high spot and is a feathered taper arrangement. See Fig. 8-2.

A chrome or nickel-plated zinc die casting—such as an auto door handle where the plating is pitted and flaked away by oxidation beneath the plating—you have no choice but to remove the part, strip off the old plating, repolish, pickle, etc., to get rid of the corrosive underlying problem that caused the plating to foul in the first place. Then you replate.

The exception to the rule would be a rather large item that you could not remove. If you could remove it you could not get it in your plating bath. Here you would have to resort to cleaning up the spot as best as possible. Sand the good plating so that it is feathered into the spot you have to plate and then brush plate.

Do it like a pro. Strip off the old plating and repolish, buff, clean, pickle, and bright dip. Plate as you would if it had never been plated before. This makes it like new. Also you might want to, for example, gold plate a nickel-plated object or silver plate a nickel-plated

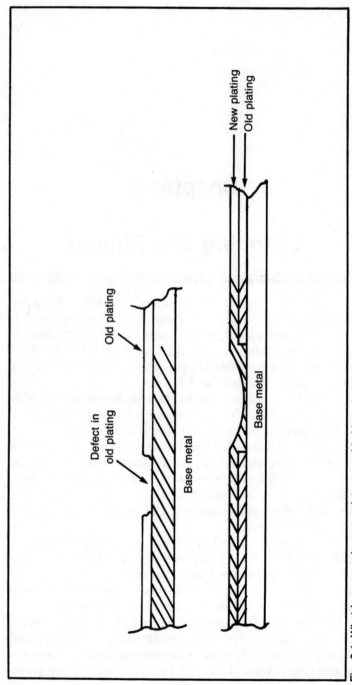

Fig. 8-1. What happens when you plate over old chipped plating.

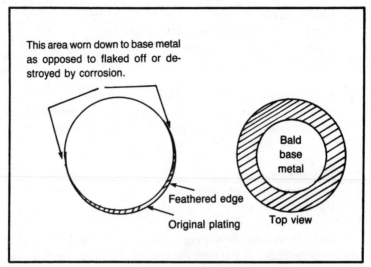

This area worn down to base metal as opposed to flaked off or destroyed by corrosion.

Bald base metal

Feathered edge

Original plating

Top view

Fig. 8-2. Plating bald spots that have a feather edge where it meets the base metal.

object. Even though the nickel plating is in good shape, you can run into problems of getting the gold plating to adhere to the underlying nickel coat. Also gold on nickel looks different than gold on copper.

Your best bet all around, regardless of the finish when plating gold, silver, nickel, chrome, an underlying copper plate will reduce most problems. Copper plating is inexpensive and easy. In addition, most base metals—steel, iron, brass, and zinc—are easily and inexpensively copper plated. The copper hangs on good and tight. The final plating of what have you will hang on to the copper plate. You would have quite a trying time getting nickel plating, chrome plating, gold plating, or silver plating to go directly on to a piece of steel or iron. If you give the steel or iron object a light copper plate (strike), however, it then becomes very easy to plate with the metal of your choice. If the object has a copper base (for gold or silver), you simply go ahead. No copper strike is necessary.

I cannot imagine someone plating a gold or silver item with nickel, chrome, copper or whatever. Gold on silver is done quite often.

COPPER PLATING FROM IRON OR STEEL

If the plate is light and thin, you can dissolve it away with a cyanide bath:

1 gallon water.
2 jiggers of hydrogen peroxide 30 percent.
4 ounces potassium cyanide.
100 degrees Fahrenheit.

A few minutes should dissolve off the copper.

Another way to remove the copper plate is to convert it chemically to a copper sulfide CuS, also called cupric sulfide. This is a simple, inexpensive way to go:

20 ounces sodium sulfide.
2 ounces flowers of sulfur.
1 gallon of water.

Boil this until the flowers of sulfur is dissolved. Let it cool to room temperature. If you soak the copper-plated item in this solution for 5 or more minutes, the copperplating is converted to copper sulfide, which is loose and can usually simply be brushed and rinsed off. It might take one or more soakings to do the trick if the copper is stubborn.

You can, after your conversion of the copper to CuS, put the item in a saturated solution of Oxone. Oxone is potassium peroxymonosulfate. In short, it's a triple salt that produces copious volumes of tiny oxygen bubbles. One of its uses is in the manufacture of false teeth cleaning tablets. A saturated solution is about 25 grams of Oxone dissolved in 100 milliliters of water. It will pick all the CuS from the item in nothing flat (similar to ultra sonic cleaning). You will find many uses for Oxone. With a lacquered surface, if soaked in a hot solution of Oxone at 100 degrees Fahrenheit, the lacquer is softened by the heat and the Oxone bubbles the rest. The Oxone decomposes releasing oxygen.

Another way to go is to leave out the flowers of sulfur in the copper-to-copper sulfide strip and use the following formula:

1 pound of sodium sulfide.
1 gallon water
Temperature 100 degrees Fahrenheit

Reverse plate the copper off in this solution at 2 volts (the work being the anode). See Fig. 8-3.

When using the conversion of copper-to-copper sulfide system, rinse the work in hot and cold water, dip in a 10-percent solution

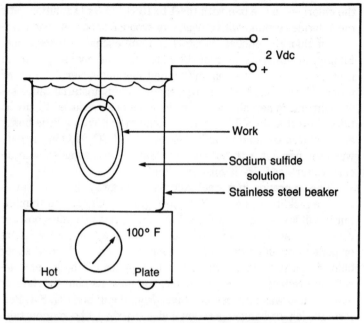

Fig. 8-3. Electrostripping off copper plating with sodium sulfide.

of cyanide, and rinse again in hot and cold water.

COPPER, ZINC, AND SILVER FROM ALUMINUM

Copper, zinc, and silver are readily soluble in nitric acid. When aluminum is immersed in nitric acid it becomes passive and will not dissolve along with the copper, zinc, or silver. To strip copper, zinc, and silver from aluminum, you dip it in a solution of 1 part nitric acid and 1 part water at 90 to 100 degrees Fahrenheit.

If you strip silver plating from any item using nitric acid, the silver is easily recovered from the nitric by adding NaCl (table salt). This drops the silver out of solution as a silver chloride AgCl (a curdy white precipitate). Filter this off and with hot water wash it free from any copper (on the filter). This chloride can be sold or reduced to metallic silver for melting to be used as an anode. If you want to reduce the silver chloride to metallic silver, it's very easy.

Take a steel gold pan and put the clean white silver chloride in the pan. Now add just enough sulfuric acid water solution to cover the chlorides: 1 part sulfuric acid, 15 parts water. Remember, never pour water into acid; pour the acid into the water. You now have the chlorides in the pan with the 1 to 15 H_2SO_4/H_2O solution. Stir the chlorides around with a plastic or wooden spoon. As each particle of chloride touches the steel pan, ion exchange takes place. Simply, the chlorine atom of the silver chloride hooks up with an iron atom to produce iron sulfide and metallic silver. The silver reduced by this method is a gray, sandy-looking material called silver cement. When all the chlorides have been reduced to silver, filter this off and wash it good. Dry and melt it with a little borax and cast it into a silver anode. Discard the H_2SO_4/H_2O in the pan, wash the pan out with hot and cold water—then some sodium bicarb water—and dry it for next time.

This operation in a steel gold pan eats away the gold pan as you are pickling the steel. Your pan will get thinner and thinner, but it will last for quite a time. You can do this in a glass bowl or casserole dish. However, you must throw in a few steel washers or nails to do the reduction. In this case, every particle of silver chloride must contact a washer or nail. When all the silver chlorides are reduced to metallic silver, you must fish out the nails or washers and wash the cement silver from them. See Fig. 8-4. Perform the ion exchange operation under an exhaust hood or outside.

CHROME PLATING FROM STEEL

You can use reverse plating or a chemical solution to strip chrome plating from steel. See Fig. 8-5. Another way to strip chrome would be to reverse plate strip in about any alkaline solution, the simplest being sodium hydroxide (lye), with 5 to 7 ounces of sodium hydroxide per gallon of water. See Fig. 8-6.

Note: Whenever you are stripping any plating from any base metal, you have to be on guard not to go overboard and pit the base metal. All you want to do is remove the old plating and not digest the base metal under the plating.

CHROMIUM FROM BRASS, COPPER OR NICKEL

Concentrated hydrochloric acid at room temperature will strip brass. See. Fig. 8-7. You can also strip chrome from a nickel base with a sulfuric-acid, reverse-plating process. However, the chrome is stripped and then the nickel starts to go. Being the same basic color, you don't know when the chrome is gone and now you are digesting the nickel base metal (the object). See Fig. 8-8.

A little slower strip for chrome plate on brass, copper, or nickel is to use 1 pint of hydrochloric acid and 1 gallon of water, temper-

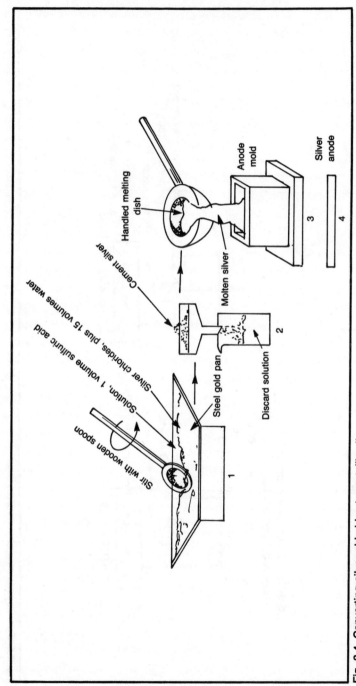

Fig. 8-4. Converting silver chlorides to metallic silver.

113

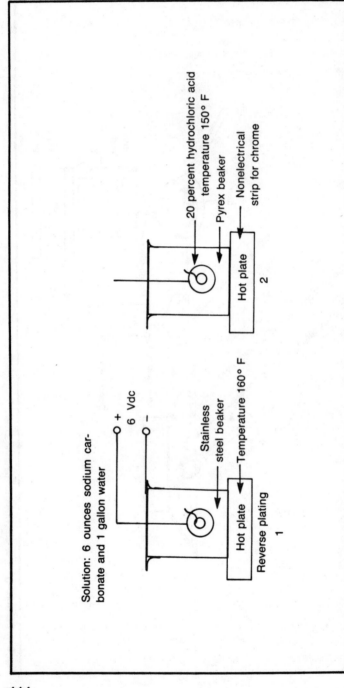

Fig. 8-5. Two ways to strip chrome from steel.

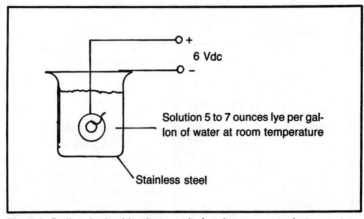

6 Vdc

Solution 5 to 7 ounces lye per gallon of water at room temperature

Stainless steel

Fig. 8-6. Sodium hydroxide electro strip for chrome on steel at room temperature.

ature 150 degrees Fahrenheit.

Chapter 7 covers the cyanide pickles and bright dips for gold and silver. As you can see, there is a close relationship between scaling, pickles, bright dips and strips for removing plating.

CYANIDE STRIPS

Let's talk about cyanide again. Because gold, silver, copper and cadmium are soluble in sodium cyanide or potassium cyanide, you have a common solution to remove any of the above metals plated on steel or iron objects. Solution:

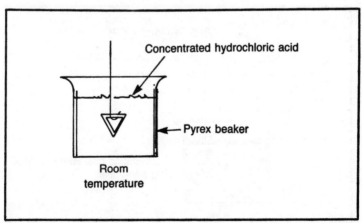

Concentrated hydrochloric acid

Pyrex beaker

Room temperature

Fig. 8-7. Nonelectrical chrome strip from brass at room temperature. Using concentrated hydrochloric acid (HC1).

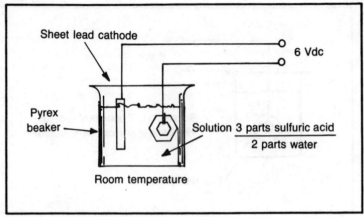

Fig. 8-8. Electrostripping chrome from nickel.

417 milliliters water (about 1 pint).

2 or 3 ounces sodium cyanide.

At room temperature in the sink, add 2 ounces of 30 percent hydrogen peroxide.

Strip only a few objects at a time to prevent a too-rapid generation of heat and gassing. Watch the item. If the gassing quits and the item is not stripped, add another dash (1 ounce) of fresh hydrogen peroxide.

If the solution starts to color up blue or becomes murky, add sufficient cyanide to clear it up. See Fig. 8-9. This procedure will

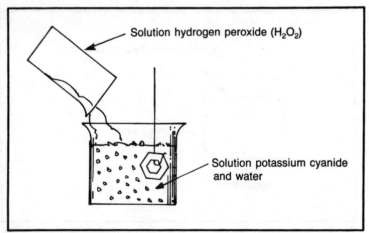

Fig. 8-9. Stripping light gold plate with cyanide and hydrogen peroxide.

116

suffice for stripping silver, gold, and copperplate.

HEAVY GOLD PLATE

Solution:

Concentrated sulfuric acid.
A pinch of chromic acid.
Lead cathode.
Object to be stripped anode.
6 volts dc.
Room temperature.

In this system, the gold leaves the object and does not go to the cathode. Instead, it simply falls to the bottom of the beaker and has to be filtered off.

You are going to invariably get some base metals involved. Watch carefully that you don't eat up the object. You simply wave to remove the gold plating. See Fig. 8-10.

LEAD PLATING OR LEAD SPLATTER

Solution:

1/2 gallon glacial acetic acid.
10 ounces hydrogen peroxide, 30 percent.
1 1/2 gallon water
Work at room temperature.

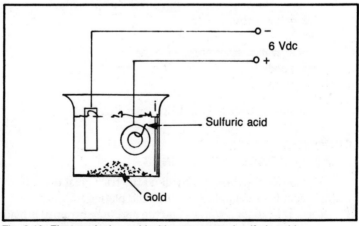

Fig. 8-10. Electrostripping gold with concentrated sulfuric acid.

Dip item into this solution until lead is removed.

Glacial Acetic Acid. The term glacial is applied to various nearly pure acids that have a freezing point slightly below room temperature. Acetic acid, when 99.8 percent pure, crystallizes at 62 degrees Fahrenheit, and is called glacial acetic acid. Acetic CH_3COOH, when it is not pure (contains water), is known as ethanoic acid or vinegar acid.

A similar lead remover, used at room temperature, but without water removes lead from silver or gold items by simple immersion of the item is as follow:

10 ounces glacial acetic acid.
1/2 ounce hydrogen peroxide, 30 percent.

REMOVING LEAD FROM STEEL

This solution—1 part by volume ammonium hydroxide and 1 part by volume water—is very basic (blue on litmus). You add to this solution a strong acetic acid (80 percent). Add the acetic acid in small increments. Check with pH papers until the solution is just neutral pH 7. Now add some more of the 80 percent acetic acid until your solution is slightly acid, pH 6 to 6.5. Work this solution at 150 degrees Fahrenheit. Dip the objects for 4 or 5 minutes or until lead is removed.

REMOVING NICKEL PLATING
FROM STEEL, BRASS, OR COPPER

1 1/2 gallon sulfuric acid.
6 volts.
1 gallon water. Room temperature.
Work anode.
Lead cathode.

A pinch of copper sulfate helps. See Fig. 8-11.

CHROME AND NICKEL
FROM ZINC-BASE DIE CASTINGS

Concentrated sulfuric acid will do the trick. Just dip it in the sulfuric acid long enough to remove the plating.

Note. If I call for a voltage and the part to be stripped is made the anode (+), this is called reverse plating or an electro strip. If you are electro stripping, make sure that the voltage is on before you enter the part to be stripped in the bath. The current is turned off only after you remove the item from the bath. Also make sure that the part to be stripped is dry.

The strips that do not call for any voltage are simply dip strips. Here again the part should be dry. Example: The chrome and nickel strip for zinc base die castings is nothing more than concentrated sulfuric acid. Remember the rule. Never add water to acid (especially H_2SO_4). It will spit back at you. If you dunk a wet part into concentrated sulfuric acid, its going to cause quite a reaction. Also it will start diluting the solution.

The rule of turning on the current first prior to entering the item into the bath and off after the part is out of the bath applies to electroplating, electro cleaning, and electro stripping.

Temperature. When I call for room temperature for the operation of a strip, bright dip, plating etc., the reference is to at least 70 degrees Fahrenheit. If your solution has cooled below this point prior to or during use, you should warm it up. Most chemical action is increased by heat. A plating solution at, say 40 degrees Fahrenheit or 60 degrees Fahrenheit will, in some cases, not work at all or slowly at best. You have, in many cases, heat produced by the chemical reaction by simply confining the various components. This heat-producing reaction is called the exothermic process.

The opposite of exothermic is called endothermic, a process accompanied by the absorption of heat—thus cooling.

Add sodium hydroxide to water and heat is produced. Add sulfuric acid to water and heat is produced.

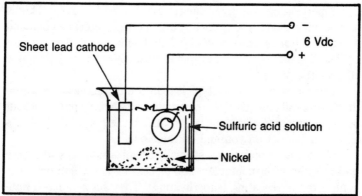

Fig. 8-11. Electrostripping nickel from steel, brass, or copper.

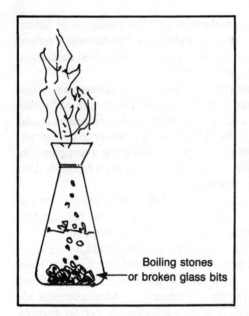

Fig. 8-12. Using boiling stones to prevent accidents.

Boiling stones or broken glass bits

When you add any chemical to any solution that produces heat, this should be done in small increments. Allow the mix to cool between additions to prevent the too-rapid accumulation of heat, which can crack the mixing container (beaker, flask, etc.). The too-rapid reaction can boil over with explosive force. This is what I refer to as high-speed chemistry.

Explosion. An explosion is defined as a violent and rapid increase of pressure in a confined space. This can be caused by an external force of energy (heat) or by an internal exothermic chemical reaction.

Superheating is a great danger overlooked by many. This is where you are trying to bring a solution (even water) to a boil and it gets to a temperature well above its boiling point, it is still not boiling, and then—bang—it erupts explosively with one big bubble all over the place.

The classic case of this type is to heat milk on the stove where the milk is still and quiet. It can get above its boiling point without boiling, you come along and stir or shake the pot, and bingo it's all out of the pot on you and on the stove.

When boiling anything, especially chemicals, always add some broken glass to the container. The pieces of glass will prevent the liquid from overheating (superheating). They act as built-in bubbles. You need just enough so that there is always some on the bottom, even with the lifting action.

You can purchase boiling stones that are essentially 99.6 percent pure silica. These stones are designed to have innumerable sharp projections for the release of vapor bubbles.

Remember, when a liquid boils the temperature must be slightly above its boiling point before bubble initiation can begin. If it doesn't begin at this point, it can superheat and begin with one giant bubble. See Fig. 8-12.

Chapter 9

Various Plating Baths

Some plating baths given here are simple and some are more complex. By and large, you will get your best results staying as simple as possible. This rule holds true also with your equipment. There is a general trend today to take something that was simple and worked well and complicate it. Don't get caught up in this. Stay low tech; keep it small and own it all. You can do a good job.

Plating baths are simply variations of each other. Like cooking recipes, one fellow calls for one toe of garlic, and another leaves out the garlic and a herb or two. Both taste as good.

The baths given here work very well and the chemicals are readily available. Prepared solutions can be purchased from a large selection of suppliers. Consult the *Thomas Register* at your local library. They list most of them. The *Thomas Register* is also a good source for polishing, buffing machines, wheels, and compounds.

You will soon notice that I vary how I list formulas. Sometimes the formula is given in ounces per gallon or grams per liter or pints per gallon. You will find conversion factors in the back of this book.

The amounts given are not critical (within limits). If I call for 4 1/2 grams of X, and you don't have a gram scale, but you have a teaspoon—well a teaspoon is roughly (level) 4.39 grams. This will work just as well. In liquid, one teaspoon is roughly 4.94 milliliters (level). If a bath calls for 5 ML, a teaspoon is close enough. Any formula that is too tight with little or no allowances belongs in a research-and-development lab. This is a common problem with R & D.

Many times a formula or process is worked out under lab conditions and it won't work in production. It's too tight. The lab technician is working in micrograms and the process is handed to someone who works in buckets and shovels full. Plating solutions are called baths or electrolytes.

Let's redefine what we are going to do with the plating solution, bath, electrolyte or whatever you want to call it. The electrolysis of an electrolyte is what you do when you electroplate.

Electrolysis, simply defined, is the chemical decomposition of certain substances (electrolytes) by an electric current passed through the substance in a dissolved state. Such substances are ionized into electrically charged ions. When an electric current is passed through them by means of conducting electrodes (cathode and anode), the ions move toward the opposite charged electrode. There they give up their electric charges and become uncharged atoms or groups of atoms.

GOLD BATHS

Prior to the development of electroplating as we know it today, articles were covered with gold leaf using the mercury process. The mercury process is simple and extremely dangerous. Don't even think of trying this.

Mercury will wet fine gold. What the guilders did was to make up a gold mercury amalgam (an alloy of mercury)—just like the dentist makes up a mercury silver amalgam to fill your teeth. This mixture of gold powder and mercury was rubbed on the item to be gilded. When the entire area you wanted to gild with gold was covered, the guilder then took a torch and heated the gold mercury coating to a temperature above the vaporizing point of the mercury 356.6 degrees Celsius. The mercury vapor usually went off into the lungs of the operator of the torch. This left the gold on the item where it was burnished to a fine finish. The fellows who did this had a working life span of about 27 years. A tough vocation.

No. 1 Gold Bath

3/4 ounce neutral gold chloride.
2 ounces Potassium Cyanide.
1 quart distilled water.
Pure gold anode.

Temperature 140 degrees Fahrenheit.

Voltage is 4 to 6 volts.

Make up this solution and let it stand for several days before using. Bath is toxic (cyanide). This bath is a simple one that works very well. See Fig. 9-1.

No. 2 Gold Bath

1/4 ounce gold chloride.

1 1/4 ounce sodium cyanide.

1/4 ounce sodium bisulfite.

1 quart distilled water.

Pure gold anode.

Temperature 140 degrees Fahrenheit.

The bath is toxic. This gold bath is more suited for heavy gold deposits than No. 1.

No. 3 Gold Bath

1/4 ounce gold cyanide.

2.5 ounces potassium cyanide.

1/2 ounce sodium phosphate.

Pure gold anode.

Temperature 140 degrees Fahrenheit

Bath toxic.

A general gold bath good color.

No. 4 Gold Bath

1 ounce gold cyanide.

1.5 ounces potassium cyanide.

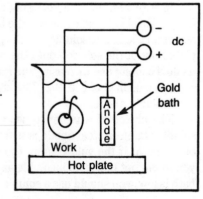

Fig. 9-1. A basic gold bath setup.

Pure gold anode.

Temperature 140 degrees Fahrenheit.

Bath toxic.

Good for heavy deposits.

No. 5 Gold Bath

6 grams potassium gold cyanide.

15 grams monosodium phosphate.

3/4 gram potassium nickel cyanide.

Pure gold anode.

Temperature 140 degrees Fahrenheit.

Voltage 2 to 3 volts.

pH 7 neutral.

No. 6 Gold Bath

3 dwt (pennyweights) gold chloride.

3 ounces sodium cyanide.

1 pinch of copper carbonate.

1 quart distilled water.

Anode 14 kt. gold.

If you are plating from a gold cyanide bath and dark streaks start to show on the anode, the free cyanide is too low. In this case, you add the appropriate pinch of cyanide KCN or NaCN to the bath. Stir between additions until the anode clears up. The anode should always be bright. If you have an excess of free cyanide in a bath, the gold plating will be too pale in color.

You can plate the gold out of the bath onto the object by using a soluble gold anode or with an insoluble anode of stainless steel. See Fig. 9-2.

In A of Fig. 9-2, the gold anode slowly dissolves during plating, replenishing gold cations to the bath. In B of Fig. 9-2, the stainless steel anode is insoluble and the gold cations in the solution are plated out of the solution onto the work, stripping the solution of its gold content and increasing the ratio of gold to free cyanide. The same is true in C of Fig. 9-2. The stainless steel beaker is used as an insoluble anode.

The choice of whether to use a soluble gold anode or an insoluble stainless steel anode is usually based on the gold content of the bath. If the gold content (gold cations) in the bath is high, you might opt to use an insoluble anode. If the gold content of the bath is low, you should use a soluble gold anode to keep the proper

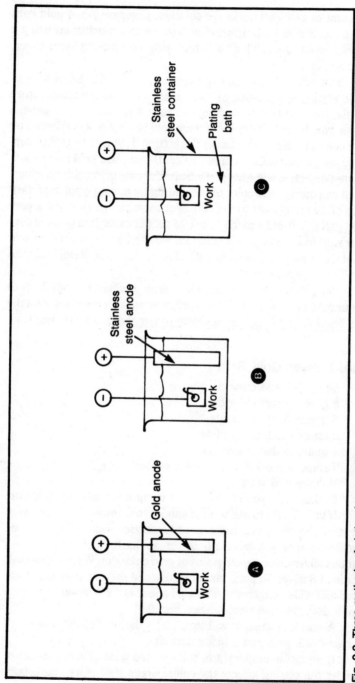

Fig. 9-2. Three methods of plating from a gold bath.

127

amount of gold cations in the solution. Compare No. 4 gold bath with No. 3 gold bath. In general, you are much better off using a soluble gold anode. This holds true with most plating baths silver, copper, etc.

You will find that you can come up with different shades of gold plating by variation of the voltage used and the temperature of the bath. This is something you have to fiddle with to get the color you desire. The color of your gold plating is also affected by the color of the material under the plating. If you plate gold to copper, the plating takes on a red color. If you plate gold to a nickel-plated object, it will give you a beautiful pale gold color on silver. You can change the color of the plating by adding a pinch of various other metal salts to the bath. For example, you will get a very red golf if you add a pinch or two of copper carbonate (a basic copper salt) to a gold cyanide solution. Remember, do not add an acid metal salt such as copper sulfate to a cyanide bath. Remember the acid and cyanide rule.

For green gold, you can add a drop of silver cyanide bath to your gold cyanide bath. Here again you must experiment with the addition voltage and temperature to get the green you want.

No. 7 Green Gold Bath

50 grains gold chloride.
8 grains silver chloride.
5 grains lead carbonate.
2 ounces sodium cyanide.
1 quart of distilled water.
Temperature 140 degrees Fahrenheit.
Voltage is 5 volts.
In this bath, you can plate out using a stainless steel anode.

If you choose to use soluble anodes to maintain the cation content of the bath, you must use two anodes—one silver and one gold—because you have a bath containing both silver cations (8 grains silver chloride, 50 grains of gold chloride). With a metal salt ratio of 8 silver 50 gold, you must use one narrow, pure silver anode and wide gold anode. The gold anode is 6 1/4 larger in surface area than the silver anode. See Fig. 9-3.

A speck of arsenic will give you a darker deposit; too much arsenic will give you a black deposit.

Here again temperature, voltage, and what kind of metals are under the plating affects the color. Green gold plated on copper

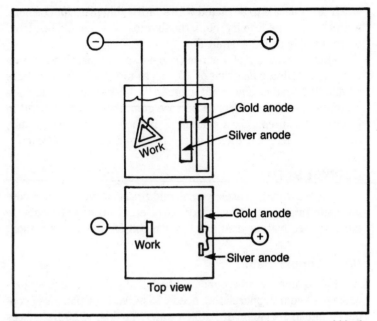

Fig. 9-3. Plating with a silver anode and a gold anode in a green, gold bath.

looks different than green gold plated on nickel. This goes for any plating bath or metal.

No. 8 Roman Gold Bath

50 grains gold chloride.
1/2 ounce sodium cyanide.
1/2 ounce sodium phosphate.
1 quart distilled water.
This bath is worked hot, 160 degrees Fahrenheit.
Pure gold anode.
Voltage is 1.5 to 2 volts.

No. 9 Rose Gold Bath

70 grains gold chloride.
1 ounce sodium cyanide.
1/4 ounce caustic soda (lye, sodium hydroxide).
1 quart distilled water.
Temperature 180 degrees Fahrenheit.
Voltage is 4 to 5 volts.
Pure gold anode.

If the object is to be plated with a rather thin plate for cosmetic reasons (costume jewelry, etc.), the thin rose gold should be plated on to what is called a smut dip.

This dip consists of 4 ounces copper sulfate dissolved in a nitric acid solution consisting of 16 ounces nitric acid in 16 ounces of distilled water. The smut solution is heated to 170 degrees Fahrenheit and the object to be rose gold plated is immersed in it until it acquires a dark coating. It is then rinsed in hot water, then cold water, and then into the rose gold bath for plating.

COPPER BATHS

In a great many cases, you should first give the object a copper plate prior to chrome, silver, gold, etc. You will no doubt do more copper plating than any other metal for the above reason.

No. 1 Copper Bath

This is an easy, all-around acid bath that will cover a great percentage of your copperplating needs. Dissolve 1 3/4 pounds of copper sulfate in 1/2 gallon of distilled water. To this, add 3 1/2 ounces of sulfuric acid. Now add enough distilled water to the above to give you a total of 1 gallon. Warm to 90 degrees Fahrenheit. Use a pure copper anode at 1.5 to 2 volts.

To this bath, you can add 1/2 ounce aluminum sulfate. This will improve the deposit somewhat.

No. 2 Copper Bath

25 ounces copper sulfate.
6 ounces sulfuric acid.
1 gallon distilled water.
Room temperature to 90 degrees Fahrenheit.
Anode pure copper.
Voltage is 2 to 5 volts.
Used for all-around copperplating.

No. 3 Bright Copper Bath

30 ounces copper sulfate.
9 ounces sulfuric acid.
1 gallon distilled water.
A smidgeon of thiourea.

Thiourea is thiocarbamide $(NH_2)_2CS$. Any chemical supply house can supply you with this.

Make up your bath #3, use a copper anode, heat the bath to 80 degrees Fahrenheit, test plate some copper onto an object, and add a few grains thiourea to your bath and test plate again. When you get a bright copper plate, don't add any more thiourea. If the plating starts getting dull after some use, add another smidgeon of thiourea. In 1 gallon of bath, you are looking at .0014 of an ounce of thiourea. If you don't have a good chemical balance, you have to feel your way. You are looking at a very small amount of thiourea. Also you want to add about as much hydrochloric acid to the bath as you do thiourea, .0014 ounce HCL voltage 2 to 5 volts.

No. 4 Bright Copper Bath

This bath is similar to No. 3. The only difference is molasses and thiourea and no hydrochloric.

27 ounces copper sulfate.
4 ounces sulfuric acid.
.005 ounces thiourea.
0.1 ounce Brer rabbit molasses (grocery store).
Temperature 70 degrees Fahrenheit to 90 degrees Fahrenheit.
Pure copper anode.
Voltage is 1 to 4 volts.

No. 5 Cyanide Copper Bath

3 ounces copper cyanide.
1.5 ounces sodium cyanide.
2 ounces sodium carbonate.
1 gallon distilled water.
Temperature 70 degrees to 100 degrees Fahrenheit.
Pure copper anode.
Voltage is 1.5 to 5 volts.
No. 5 gives a good, smooth plate of good color.

No. 6 Cyanide Copper Bath

16 ounces sodium cyanide.
8 ounces copper carbonate.
2 ounces sodium carbonate.
1 gallon distilled water.
Pure copper anode.

Temperature 80 degrees Fahrenheit.
Voltage 3 to 4 volts.

Alternate to Bath No. 6

9 1/2 ounces sodium cyanide.
6 3/4 ounces copper carbonate.
3 ounces sodium bisulfate.
1 gallon distilled water.
Use as for bath No. 6.

Should the copperplating from a cyanide bath become a dull red color or plate unevenly, this condition can usually be corrected with the following brightening solution.

Brightening Solution for Copper Cyanide Baths

Dissolve 1 1/2 ounces lead carbonate in 16 ounces of warm, distilled water. Now add 3 ounces of caustic soda (lye), stir this solution until it is clarified, and then add 1 ounce of cream of tartar, and stir. Filter this solution into a dark bottle, cap, and label it "cyanide copper bath brightener." When needed, only use a few drops in a 1 gallon copper cyanide bath to correct things. Too much will result in a grayish colored plating.

To get the lead carbonate into the 16 ounces of distilled water, you are going to have to make a paste of your 1 1/2 ounces with a little of your distilled water. Lead carbonate is toxic.

When you get into the section on plating nonconductors—such as leaves, bugs, baby shoes—where you use a silver conductor copperplate first and then thin silver or gold. The first copperplate must be done from an acid copper bath. Copper bath No. 1, 2, 3, or 4 will do the job. If you use a cyanide copper bath, it will dissolve the silver conductor coat. After you have covered the silver conductor coat with copper from an acid copper bath, you can plate silver or gold on this copper coat from any cyanide bath.

SILVER BATHS

Unless you are going to silverplate pewter on top of a tin or nickelplate, you should always copperplate the object first. About 99 percent of all silverplating today is done from cyanide silver baths. They have good throwing power and produce superior work.

No. 1 Silver Cyanide Bath

    6 ounces sodium cyanide.

    3 ounces silver chloride.

    1 gallon distilled water.

When you have the sodium cyanide and silver chloride dissolved in the 1 gallon of distilled water, add 6 ounces sodium carbonate. The addition of the sodium carbonate gives the bath very good throwing power and produces a fine-grain plating.

Should you decide to make the bath without the sodium carbonate, change the formula to:

    8 ounces sodium cyanide.

    3 ounces silver chloride.

    1 gallon distilled water.

Both formulas are operated at 1 to 2 volts at room temperature, 70 degrees Fahrenheit. With any silver bath using silver chloride, it is much less expensive to make your own silver chloride using the following method. You can make silver chloride from old silver jewelry or sterling silver scrap on pure silver scrap.

Step 1. Melt the scrap with the torch in a hand-melting dish with a pinch of borax. See Fig. 9-4.

Step 2. When the silver is melted and very fluid, it is poured from a distance of 2 feet into a steel bucket full of cold water. This granulates the silver, giving it a high surface area. See Fig. 9-5.

Step 3. The granulated silver prepared in Step 2 is removed from the water and placed in a beaker, to which is added a solution consisting of 1 volume of nitric acid. Three volumes of distilled water. Just enough to cover the granulated silver by about 1/2 inch. See Fig. 9-6.

The beaker with the silver granules and the nitric-water solution is warmed under the hood. The nitric acid water solution will start to dissolve the silver granules and give off nitrous oxide fumes that are reddish brown. These fumes are called "nox" and are quite toxic. The work must be done in a fume hood. As long as the solution is working, these fumes will be given off. As long as there is silver to be dissolved and free acid to work on it, you will see action. "Nox" and each piece of silver will be sending up a stream of bubbles. See Fig. 9-7.

When all the silver has been digested by virtue that there is no longer a metal particle on the bottom of the beaker giving off a bubble trail, dilute the solution left in the beaker with 2 volumes of distilled water. See Fig. 9-8.

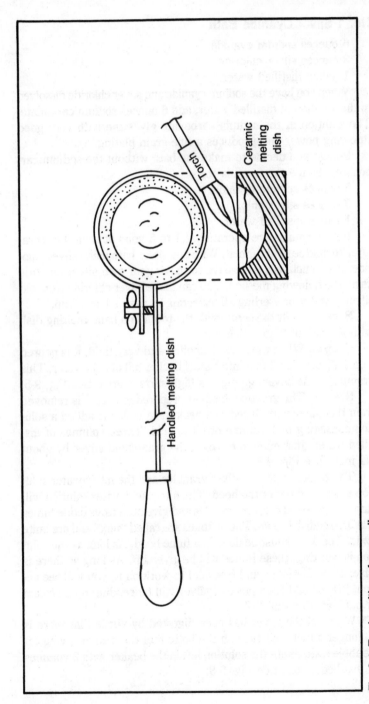

Fig. 9-4. Torch melting of scrap silver.

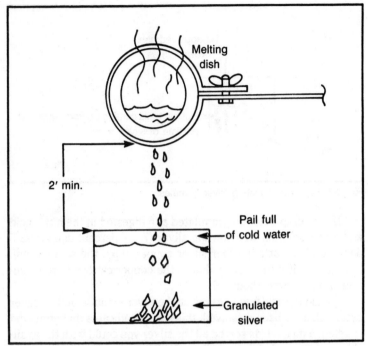

Fig. 9-5. Molten silver is granulated by pouring it into cold water.

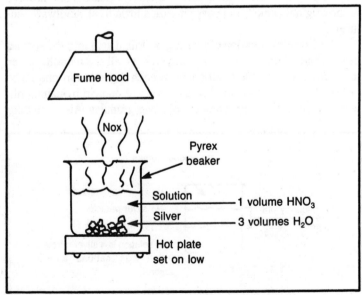

Fig. 9-6. Digesting granulated silver in dilute nitric acid.

135

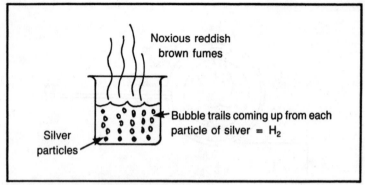

Fig. 9-7. Action of digesting silver granules.

If the scrap that you granulated and digested in the nitric acid and water solution was sterling silver (7 1/2 percent copper 92.5 percent silver) or any other silver copper alloy, the solution will have a definite green color due to the copper cations in the solution. Don't worry about this.

Should the acid quit working on the silver granules in the beaker before all have been dissolved, this simply indicates that your acid is killed. You have dissolved all the silver you could with the available acid you added to your silver. In this case, pour the killed acid off into another clean beaker. Leave the silver that did not dissolve in the original beaker and cover it with a little fresh acid/water solution.

Repeat this operation of pouring off killed acid into the second beaker and adding fresh acid until you have all the metallic silver in solution and all the solution from each digestion in one large beaker. If you do it in small steps, you save on acid by using only what you need for a given amount of silver granules. Also, you take

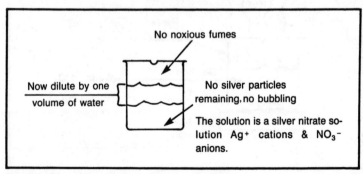

Fig. 9-8. Completion of silver granules digestion.

less risk of a boil over or the evolution of more fumes than your hood can quickly handle.

Step 4. You now have a solution free of silver metallic particles. This solution consists of a silver nitrate solution and copper nitrate solution (a soup of silver cations and copper cations). Now make up a saturated salt solution (table salt) in warm distilled water (about a pint). Use all the salt you can dissolve in 1 pint of distilled water. Label this "concentrated sodium chloride solution."

Put your solution from your silver digestion (your soup) in a large beaker or glass pitcher. Now add a squirt of your concentrated sodium chloride solution to this. You will at once see a curdy white precipitation drop out of your soup. This is your silver chlorides. See Fig. 9-9.

Let the chlorides settle to the bottom of your pitcher or beaker. Then add another squirt of your salt solution and see if anymore chlorides fall. If so, let them settle and repeat until you get no new precipitation with an addition of your salt solution. Let this all settle and decanter off the top solution without disturbing the chlorides. A good rule is to let the precipitation of chlorides settle overnight prior to decanting off the top liquid. This liquid goes to waste.

Step 5. Next morning wash the chlorides off on to a filter with a wash bottle. See Fig. 9-10.

If the material was sterling silver or any other copper silver

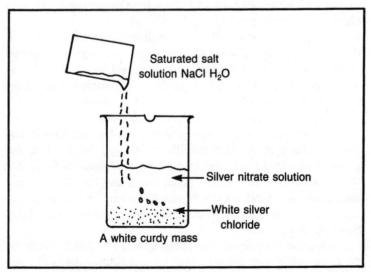

Fig. 9-9. Precipitating the silver out of the solution as a silver chloride.

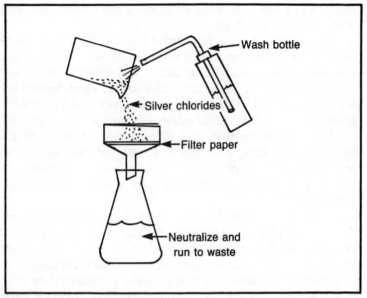

Fig. 9-10. Filtering off the silver chlorides.

alloy, you would see green color throughout the chlorides on the filter (Fig. 9-10).

Step 6. Leaving the discolored silver chlorides on the filter (Fig. 9-10), pour enough boiling hot distilled water over the chlorides until they are all pure white (free from any green or greenish blue color). See Fig. 9-11.

This hot washing does two things. It removes the copper from the silver chlorides, plus any lead chlorides that might have gotten in the act (Fig. 9-5). Perhaps a spot of lead solder stuck to our silver jewelry. Lead chlorides are soluble in hot water but the silver chlorides are only soluble in very, very hot water.

Step 7. You now have the silver chlorides on a filter paper washed free of any copper-carrying solution (copper nitrate) and any lead chlorides. Remove the filter containing the chlorides and place the unfolded filter paper on a pad of newspapers to dry. Place the newspapers with the filter paper containing the chlorides in a dark place or cabinet for the drying operation. The chlorides are light sensitive and will go from a light blue to a black in the light. See Fig. 9-12.

When the chlorides are dry, transfer them to a dark brown wide-mouthed bottle with a good tight cap. Label this silver chlorides (AgCl) for making up silver cyanide plating baths. Keep the bottle—

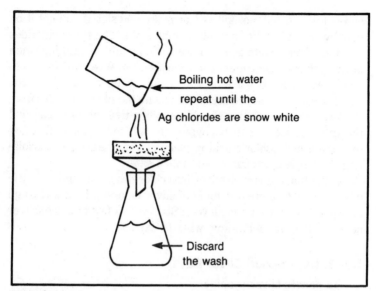

Fig. 9-11. Washing the silver chlorides free of any copper nitrate solution and any lead chlorides with hot water.

marked toxic—stored in the dark.

Silver chlorides are toxic. If they get on your skin they color the skin blue where they make contact. This area soon turns purple, brown, and then black. These stains on your skin are impossible to remove. Only time will do the trick. It takes about a week to two weeks for them to go away (by skin replacement).

The silver nitrate solution from Step 4 will also stain your skin

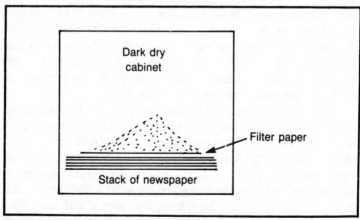

Fig. 9-12. Drying the washed chlorides.

139

and is toxic. It will not kill you or make you sick if you get it on you, but it sure makes a great looking stain. The silver chlorides and the silver nitrate solution are toxic mainly by oral ingestion or through open cuts or abrasions on the skin. Wear rubber gloves and wash these off while on your hands when you are finished.

The salt solution you use to precipitate the silver chlorides from the silver nitrate solution should be iodine-free salt. You can find this in any grocery. You can bypass the salt and do the same thing by adding hydrochloric acid in place of your saturated salt solution. Salt is less expensive and much safer.

Don't make up much silver into chlorides at one time. A little silver produces a great volume of silver chloride. Best way to go is to practice in a very small way. Start with a few grams of silver scrap so that you will know what to expect.

No. 2. High Speed Silver Bath

12 ounces silver cyanide.
12 ounces potassium cyanide.
2 ounces potassium carbonate.
3 ounces potassium hydroxide.
2 to 3 volts.
100 degrees Fahrenheit.

NICKEL BATHS

Nickel plating has taken a back seat to chromium plating. That is a shame. Nickel-plated objects have a very pleasing color. When you compare a chromium-plated object with a nickel-plated object, you will see what I mean. Nickel is not as stark as chromium.

Chromium has a thin, somewhat porous plating. When deposited over copper, it is apt to flake off due to oxygen getting to the copper through the pores of the chromium and causing the damage. No doubt you have seen chrome plated objects with large sections flaked off, exposing the under plating.

You should always copperplate and then go with gold, silver, nickel or what have you. Lots of items you plate with nickel are steel, and should you go directly onto the steel with the nickel, in short order, you will find the nickel flaking off due to spots of rust developing on the steel. This is a problem even with a copperplate on the steel and then the nickel. If you want a fine, long-lasting beautiful nickelplate on a steel item, first plate it with zinc. Then you scratch brush it with a soft brass wire wheel or hand brush.

(Jewelers supply or plating supply houses are sources.) This gives the zinc a tooth for the next plating (which should be copper then your nickel). Use high-quality nickel on steel plate, zinc, scratch brush lightly, copperplate, and then nickel.

In an effort to plate inexpensively and quickly, with no thought as to how long the plating will last, the trend is to simply plate the nickel on the item. You can still find items that were nickel plated 50 years ago and in great shape today. Investigation of these items will reveal that the item, if steel, was first plated with zinc (as a rust stopper), then copper plated, and lastly nickel. This is also true of old chromium-plated items.

No. 1 Nickel Bath

15 ounces nickel ammonium sulfate.
1 gallon of distilled water.
2 to 2 1/2 volts.
Room temperature to 100 degrees Fahrenheit.
Pure nickel anode.
This formula goes way back.

No. 2 Nickel Bath

8 ounces nickel ammonium sulfate.
4 ounces nickel sulfate.
1 to 2 ounces ammonium chloride.
1 gallon of distilled water.
Room temperature to 100 degrees Fahrenheit.
Pure nickel anode.
2 1/2 volts.
Note: Ammonium chloride is also called sal ammoniac.

No. 3 Nickel Bath

12 ounces nickel ammonium sulfate.
2 ounces boric acid.
2 ounces sodium chloride (table salt)
100 degrees Fahrenheit.
2 to 2 1/2 volts.
Pure nickel anode.
1 gallon distilled water.

This is a popular bath to use for all-around nickel plating. A good way to keep it in shape is to make up the formula just as given above. Instead, use 1 quart of distilled water in place of the 1 gallon given. Place this concentrated bath in a dark glass bottle and label it "nickel replenishing solution." It is used to pep or rejuvenate the No. 3 bath when it starts to slow down. Simply add it by drops until you have added enough to get your bath working as well as it did when new and fresh.

When your plating baths are not in use, don't let them sit around in open beakers or tanks to evaporate and collect dust. Bottle them up tightly. When a bath has been used over and over (collecting various particles of dust), filter the junk out. A couple of coffee filters will usually do the trick. When you filter your solution, always run some distilled water through the filter paper last so that you don't lose any metallic salt values on the filter. This could be costly with a gold bath. See Fig. 9-13.

When making up any plating bath—when it calls for 1 gallon of distilled water or 1 liter of distilled water or any other volume of distilled water—the reference is to the total volume of all the components going into the formula. The usual method is to take half of the volume of distilled water called for and add the metallic salts, cyanide, acid, or whatever the formula calls for. Warm this up, while stirring with a glass rod, until everything is in solution.

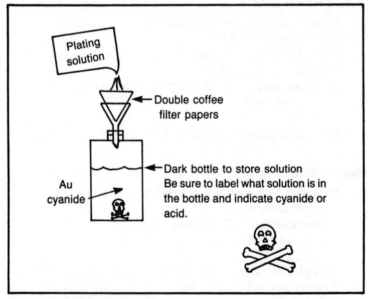

Fig. 9-13. Filter all plating baths when you are finished with them and store in a dark bottle.

Then add sufficient distilled water to make the volume called for in the formula. For example, to make up No. 3 nickel bath:

12 ounces nickel ammonium sulfate.

2 ounces boric acid.

2 ounces sodium chloride.

Stir until everything is in solution (dissolved). Now add 1 or 2 quarts of distilled water in the amount required to give you a total bath volume of 1 gallon.

When using any plating bath you lose water to evaporation. This concentrates the salts. Therefore, you must add distilled water from time to time to maintain the original bath volume.

No. 4 Fast Nickel Bath

2 pounds nickel sulfate.

4 ounces ammonium chloride.

4 ounces boric acid.

1 gallon distilled water.

Voltage is 3 1/2 volts.

Anode pure nickel.

Temperature 100 degrees Fahrenheit.

No. 5 Fast Nickel Bath

12 ounces nickel sulfate.

4 ounces nickel chloride.

2 ounces boric acid.

1 gallon distilled water.

Temperature 100 degrees Fahrenheit.

Pure nickel anode.

With this bath, start off plating with 5 volts for the first three or four minutes and then drop the voltage back to 2 volts for the remaining time.

No. 6 Low-Maintenance Nickel Bath

This bath is a workhorse and can be used for considerable time without any additions of your nickel replenishing solution.

24 ounces nickel sulfate.

3 ounces ammonium sulfate.

1 1/2 ounces magnesium sulfate.

3 ounces boric acid.

1 gallon distilled water.

Temperature 100 degrees Fahrenheit.

2 to 5 volts.

Anode pure nickel.

Nickel baths operate at relatively low voltages and many will operate at room temperature. However, heat promotes good throwing power as it decreases the resistance of the bath. Too low a voltage results in a hard, brittle deposit. Too high a voltage and the plating will be dull. You should get a good, visible plate in about three minutes if all is well.

The big thing that will give you problems with nickel baths is the pH of the bath. When you test the bath with litmus paper, the paper should show only slightly red. A pH of about 5.0 is a good spot.

You will find many references that state most nickel baths should be operated at neutral pH 7. However, if the bath moves over to the base side 8, or 9, etc., the plating will have a dull, yellowish color. It is much harder for the bath to move from a slightly acidic pH of 5.0 to a base pH 8 or 9 than to move over to a base from neutral pH 7. An indicator of the bath moving over to the basic pH is an accumulation of hydrogen bubbles on the work. See Fig. 9-14.

Like with anything you do, you have to fiddle around to get it to perform. There is no way I can give you any cut-and-dried rules or formulas. Because it is a chemical electroplating process, things are continuously changing. You have lots of variables in voltage, temperature, and bath composition.

I could give you very complicated bath formulas for nickel or

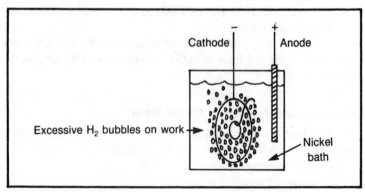

Fig. 9-14. Excessive hydrogen bubbles on work with a nickel bath indicates it is moving toward the basic side.

any other metal, but when you do this you compound the things that could go wrong. You then get into a condition where the degree of control required to keep things working correctly is usually beyond the ability of a practical plater. Some formulations will tax a skilled chemist.

Stay low tech. With all the high tech, I fail to see any better or superior plating than was produced with low tech 50 or 60 years ago. Keep it simple. The more components in the bath the more things there are to go wrong.

CHROMIUM BATH

With chromium plating, you need only one bath that is pretty well standardized. What you are after with chromium is a mirror-bright chrome coating straight from the bath. With chromium, the metal is reduced onto the object being plated directly from the bath, using an insoluble lead anode. The bath consists of only three ingredients: sulfuric acid, chromic acid, and distilled water.

33 ounces chromic acid.

.33 ounce sulfuric acid.

1 gallon distilled water.

Temperature 110 to 115 degrees Fahrenheit.

Anode sheet lead.

Current is 1 ampere for each square inch of surface to be plated.

Now, let's talk about the two most important factors involved in chromium plating: temperature and current in amperes. Unlike most plating baths that will operate over a broad range of temperatures, the chromium bath will not produce the desired brilliant deposit. You have to have a thermometer and maintain the bath temperature at 110 degrees Fahrenheit minimum 115 degrees Fahrenheit maximum. This is quite a tight (5-degree) range. You can purchase thermostatically controlled immersion heaters from platers' supply houses and chemical supply houses. The immersion heater must be the fused quartz sheath type due to the corrosive nature of the sulfuric acid and chromic acid. Otherwise you would dissolve your heater element. See Fig. 9-15.

The current of 1 ampere per square inch is quite high. By ohm's law:

$$I = \frac{E}{R}$$

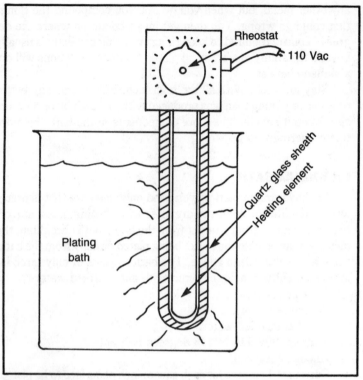

Fig. 9-15. Shielded immersion electric heater for plating baths.

I = Amperage
E = Voltage
R = The resistance in OHMS

For previous baths, I have not given the amperage but the plating voltage for operating the bath. It's not of much consequence as it is with chromium.

If "I," the amperage, is the voltage divided by the resistance of the bath to the voltage applied across it and it is high, then you will have to apply more voltage in order to get the necessary 1 ampere per square inch of surface to be plated. See Fig. 9-16.

In Fig. 9-16, let's say we have as an article to be plated 1-inch-square copperplate. Its going to take 1 ampere of current to do the job. The resistance of the solution will vary by how far away the cathode is from the work. If they are close, the resistance would be less. Therefore, it would take less voltage applied across the circuit to show 1 ampere of current flow.

The other side of the coin if the distance is increased then the

146

resistance between the work and the anode is greater. Then more voltage would have to be applied to give us our 1 ampere. The temperature of the bath will also affect its resistance.

So you have the formulation of the bath, its temperature, and the distance from the anode to the object being plated all affecting the current flow in amperes. With all this going on, how could you give a voltage recommended for chromium plating (as I give for gold or silver baths)? The voltage is considered the pressure and the amperage the rate of flow. If the resistance to the flow is high, you must increase the voltage (pressure) in order to get the amperes (flow) desired and vice versa. In our case, we need 1 ampere of flow for every square inch of area. One ampere equals 6×10^{18} electrons going by a given point each second.

If you turn the rheostat in Fig. 9-16 setup until the ampere meter reads 1 ampere (flow), you are going to get a bright chromium deposit on the 1-square-inch copperplate. If you change the plate to a surface area of 2 square inches, then you must up the voltage (pressure) to the point where you have 2 amperes of electron flow giving us 6×10^{18} electrons for each square inch surface ($2 \times 6 \times 10^{18}$) or 12,000,000,000,000,000,000 electrons.

It becomes obvious that if it takes 1 ampere per square inch to cause sufficient chromium cations to reduce to chromium metal on each square inch of your object, then if your object has 100 square inches of surface area it would take 100 amperes of elec-

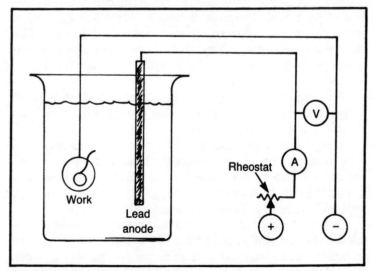

Fig. 9-16. Basic chrome plating setup.

tron flow to do the trick. Here you are looking at a fairly high amperage. From this you can readily see it takes a husky power source capable of delivering or handling sufficient amperage to do any chromium plating of any area. If you had a power source capable of delivering 100 amperes without burning up or melting, the biggest sheet of copper that you could plate on both sides would measure 7.07 × 7.07 inches.

The amperage rating of your power source dictates the size in surface area you can plate with chromium. Most power sources, dc rectifiers for gold, copper, silver are in the range from 25 amperes to 75 amperes. These baths offer little resistance to current flow.

If you estimate the square-inch area of an auto bumper, you will get a good idea of the capacity of the dc power source in amperes required to do the job.

With copper and nickel, silverplating there is only a small generation of hydrogen (bubbles at the (cathode) work). If you crank up the voltage to the point where the cathode is giving off copious hydrogen bubbles when plating with gold or silver, you are going to get a black burned deposit. Usually you adjust the voltage to the point where there is no visible evidence of hydrogen generation at the cathode.

Not so with chromium plating. With silver, gold, or copper, the bulk of the current is used exclusively in depositing the metal (reduction of cations to metallic atoms). With chromium, 85 percent of the current (amperes) is used exclusively (expended) in producing copious amounts of hydrogen gas around the work. This volume of hydrogen is so great that the hydrogen leaves the surface of the bath with such force it sprays the bath into the air. See Fig. 9-17.

With chromium plating, your beaker or tank must be much deeper than the volume of bath so that you don't spray the bath all over the place. See Fig. 9-18.

Also, the chromium bath is very corrosive (chromic acid). You must be sure the current is on before you enter the item to be plated into the bath. Otherwise the chromic acid will attack the base metal and pit it badly. With the current on, go into the chromium bath with lead anode (+). Then work piece cathode (−).

Because you are reducing the metallic chromium from the chromic acid in your bath and not from a chromium anode, you must replace the chromium removed from the bath during plating. When the bath starts to slow down or stops depositing chromium at the

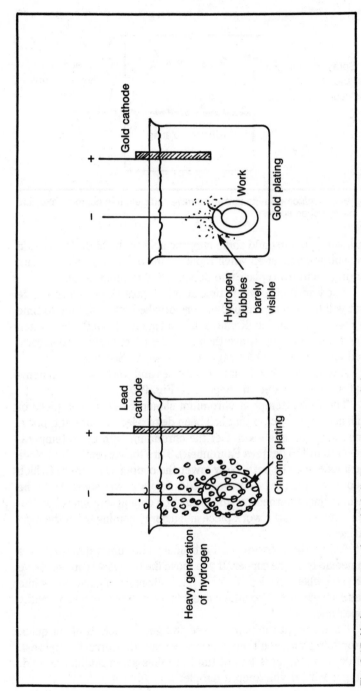

Fig. 9-17. Hydrogen generation goldplating versus chromeplating.

149

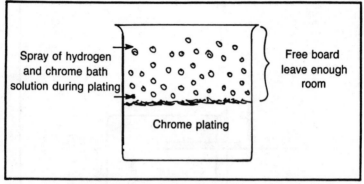

Fig. 9-18. A chromeplating tank must have sufficient free board to take care of the hydrogen spray.

cathode, you must add some chromic acid to the bath. Do not add any sulfuric acid at all when replenishing a working solution with chromic acid (to replace the deposited chromium metal).

The lead anodes will in time acquire a coating of lead chromate that will have to be scraped or wire brushed off from time to time to keep them working. Remove the lead anodes from the bath when you are not plating. Rinse them and set them aside. Use several lead anodes to give coverage to your work. See Fig. 9-19.

A sleeve anode will hit from all sides and works well with items that are complicated in shape. See Fig. 9-20.

The first attempt at chromium should be done on a piece of polished copper scrap that has been degreased and bright dipped. One inch square is good. Get the chromium bath up to temperature (110 to 115 degrees Fahrenheit). Turn the current on and place the anode into the bath. Now lower the copper work piece (which is connected to the (–) cathode side of your power source) into the bath. Adjust the rheostat until you get a copious amount of hydrogen bubbling on the work piece and a spray coming off of the bath surface.

Adjust the rheostat until a brilliant chromium deposit forms immediately on the copper. If you move the (increase) current above the point where the deposit formed is brilliant, it will take on a white matte appearance. Too little current (decrease) will give you a milky appearance.

Once you hit the point where you get a quick, brilliant quick chromium plate, don't increase or decrease the current (amperes). Chromium plating is lots of fun but takes some fiddling around. It's not hard if you keep it simple.

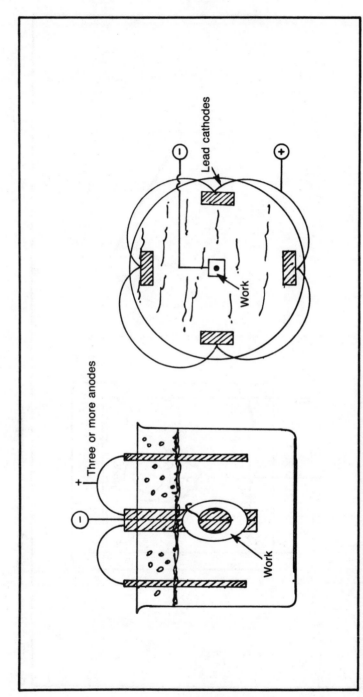

Fig. 9-19. Using multiple anodes for best results in chromeplating.

151

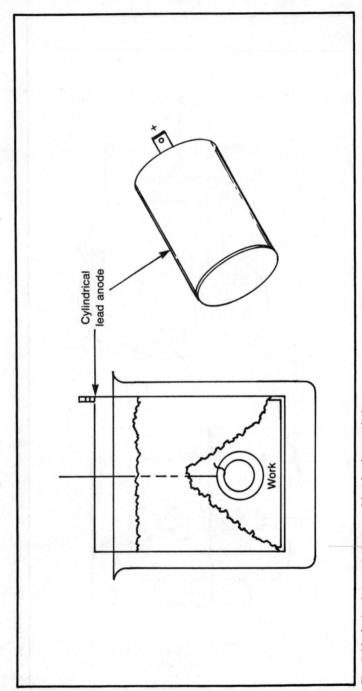

Cylindrical lead anode

Work

Fig. 9-20. A circular anode is a good bet in chromeplating.

LEAD BATH

As lead quickly tarnishes, it would not do for a decorative plate and should never be used to plate any food or drink container. You will probably never have the occasion or use for lead plating, but for the record I will give you one simple good working bath.

Dissolve 6 or 7 ounces of sodium hydroxide in a quart of distilled water. Now dissolve in this 1 to 1 1/2 ounces of lead oxide (litharge) and 1/4 ounce of gum arabic. When everything is in solution, add sufficient distilled water to make 1 gallon. Voltage is 2 to 3 volts. Anode is sheet lead. The temperature is 160 degrees Fahrenheit.

TIN BATHS

Tin is a bright plate and is what you see on tin cans. The can is steel plated with tin. Cheap objects such as tin whistles and novelties are tin plated because it is inexpensive and the results are brilliant with good corrosion resistance.

No. 1 Tin Bath

6 ounces tin chloride.
6 ounces ammonium oxalate.
1 ounce oxalic acid.
1 ounce dextrin or molasses.
1 gallon distilled water.
Temperature 140 to 150 degrees Fahrenheit.
Voltage 2 to 3 volts.
Anode tin metal or stainless steel.

If you use stainless steel as an anode, you will strip the bath of tin cations. Therefore, you will need to add tin chloride to replenish the tin content of your bath.

No. 2 Tin Bath

12 ounces sodium stannate.
2 ounces sodium acetate.
1 ounce sodium hydroxide (lye).
1 gallon distilled water.
Temperature 140 to 150 degrees Fahrenheit.
Voltage 5 volts.

Tin chloride is also called stannous chloride. The word stannous refers to containing bivalent tin. Stannic chloride would be

$SnCl_4$ (tin metal dissolved in hydrochloric acid).

The crystallized product from tin dissolved in hydrochloric acid would be the tin chloride (stannous chloride, tin salt, tin dichloride) $SnCl_2$ white crystals.

Sodium Stannate. If you dissolve tin oxide (SnO) in a strong solution of sodium hydroxide (lye) and evaporate this solution, you wind up with sodium stannate (Na_2SnO_3) light tan crystals.

If you use too high a voltage in tin plating, the deposit will be dull, spongy, and gray, and it will not adhere very well.

All plating involves ion exchange. Most metals can be put into solution. When the metal is converted to a salt of the metal, which is soluble in water, you will be able to work up all kinds of baths. All the baths given in this book are tried and true.

Chapter 10

Electroforming

Electroforming is the production or reproduction of articles by electro deposition of metal (plating). What it amounts to is if you plate an expendable form (male or female) with a plating thick enough, you can remove the expendable form by melting out or chemically dissolving it. Then you have an electroformed object. For our first example, you will produce a sheet of copper foil by electroforming it.

With a section of brass pipe or brass seamless tubing, what you want to do is form a copper foil (by plating) on the brass in such a manner that it can be removed. If you were to plate the brass tube (or form) as is, you could not remove the plate (foil) formed. In order to do this you must render the surface of your form so that it is still electrically conductive, but that the electrodeposit will not adhere to it. Plating will not attach itself to a patinaed surface but current will readily pass through a patina (oxidized surface).

Polish the brass form and clean it well. Now paint it with a solution of potassium sulfide (liver of sulfur, drugstore item) until the polished surface is patinaed to a dark sulfided surface. Hang the form in the copperplating tank and plate the entire surface copper. The thickness will be determined by the time left in the tank. For your first attempt, plate for five minutes. Remove the form with its copper coat, wash and dry, polish the copper coat on a soft buff with a little red rouge, clean, and then wipe off with a little lighter fluid. Cut a seam down the entire length with an X-Acto knife or razor and you will find that it can be easily peeled from the form as a sheet of very fine copper foil. See Fig. 10-1.

For your second attempt, plate first with silver, wash, and then plate with copper. You wind up with a piece of foil that is silver on one side and copper on the other. You can make a good, inexpensive gold foil by plating first with copper and then gold. This foil can be used for inlaying or signs. Let your imagination run on this one and you will come up with many ideas and variations. Sheet continuous foil is made industrially by electroforming with high-speed machinery.

Next, polish a bright steel nail. Give it a pink, thin copper plate from the point to a distance of say 1 inch in a cyanide copper bath. Wash in hot running water and continue plating it in your acid copper bath for 10 to 15 minutes. Wash and drop it into a jar and cover it with a strong solution of alum and water. In the morning, the nail will be gone and you will have a short, pointed, copper electroformed tube.

Now let's electroform an inlayed design of silver on copper. What you are going to do here is first electroetch a design on your copper (remove metal) and then replace the removed (copper) metal with silver metal.

Take a 2-inch square of sheet copper and polish it brightly on the buff. Clean it thoroughly. The design you want to etch and then (inlay) is painted carefully on your copper with a paint made of white lead added to a thin glue solution to form a paint of good flowing consistency. See Fig. 10-2.

Allow the design to dry thoroughly. Now coat the entire area of exposed copper and the attached copper wire with a copal varnish colored with a little chrome yellow (from any art supply store).

The copal varnish is called a resist and any surface covered with it will not be etched or plated. With acid baths, you can use asphaltum paint (hardware store) or some asphalt dissolved in benzene.

When everything is good and dry, lay the plate in a shallow glass dish of diluted nitric acid and the painted design will quickly dissolve, leaving the bare metal (copper) exposed. Now etching is the exact opposite of plating. In this case, you make the workpiece the anode and use a piece of copper for the cathode. You are going to etch or eat away your design.

You now etch the design in your acid copper bath as if you were plating (only you have reversed the polarity). The design is now your anode and the anode is your cathods. You inspect the work

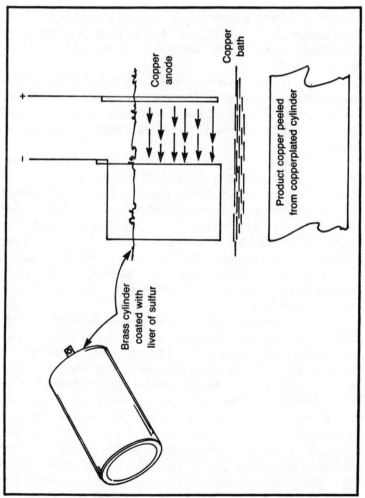

Fig. 10-1. Making copper foil by electroplating.

Copper anode

Copper bath

Product copper peeled from copperplated cylinder

+

−

Brass cylinder coated with liver of sulfur

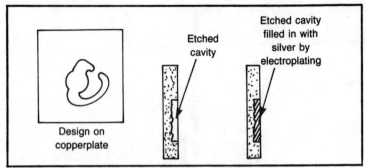

Fig. 10-2. Etched surface electro inlaid with silver.

from time to time to ascertain the depth of etch or bite. Three-thousandths of an inch is suitable for most work. When you have your design etched to your satisfaction, remove it from the bath and wash well.

All that is left to do now is to fill in the etched design back to its original level with silver. This you do by simply making it the cathode. Use a silver anode and, in your silver cyanide bath, plate in the etched design with silver. Wash, remove the resist, and polish.

Here you can probably think of 1000 variation designs and applications to etch and inlay. If you don't etch the design at all and simply plate the exposed design, you have what is known as an overlay or raised design. Now you could etch, inlay silver, then overlay a design on top of the silver in gold or just overlay on an overlay with some unplated etching. There is no end of variations or metals involved. You can etch silver, inlay it with gold, etc.

Let's make an electroformed copy of a medallion or foreign coin. In this exercise, you can use commercial electrotyper's wax or make your own.

Dissolve 5 ounces of rosin in 10 ounces of turpentine. Slowly add this solution to 10 ounces of melted beeswax while stirring. When mixed well, add 1 pound of fine graphite. Be careful here because of fire. You have a flammable solution while it is hot.

Pour some wax in a shallow container. Before the wax is completely hard, dust the face of the coin you want to electroform with fine graphite. Press this face into the still-soft wax. When removed you have a female cavity, it is a reproduction in reverse of the face. When the wax is hard, coat the inside of the cavity with a silver conductor composition (Du Pont #4817) thinned out with buytal acetate. Use a fine artist brush and give it only a very thin coat. Carry

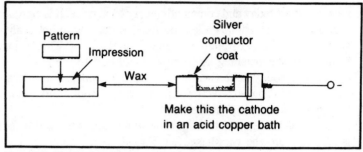

Fig. 10-3. Electro forming in a wax negative.

the coat out of the cavity onto the flat in one spot, where you can attach your plating wire. See Fig. 10-3.

Now give the cavity a light copper plate (a light pink) in an acid bath. When using a silver conductor, you must always first copper strike in an acid bath or acid nickel bath. Any cyanide bath will dissolve the conductor. Wash and transfer into a gold or silver cyanide bath and plate to the desired thickness. The initial copper strike can be removed by dissolving it in a dilute sulfuric acid solution. See Fig. 10-4.

The two faces can be electroformed and soldered together or a single-faced medallion can be soldered to a disc. Beautiful hollow jewelry can be formed by goldplating over male or female wax forms (conductor coated) or over soft metal, low-melting bismuth alloys (Cerrobend) that are melted out after the piece is formed.

Fine jewelry has been made for many years by electroforming. A lot of antique jewelry was produced this way, but it is al-

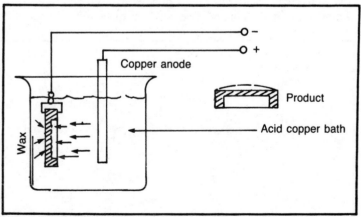

Fig. 10-4. Plating set up for item shown in Fig. 10-3.

most a lost art today and commands a very good price. It is common practice to fill the hollow electroformed jewelry with hot sealing wax with a syringe through a small hole in the back. This is done to increase the crushing strength and add heft to the piece.

As you see, you can work with positive or negative forms—metal or wax. You can electroform over copper forms and dissolve the copper form with sulfuric acid.

For hollow figures, the figure is sculpted of wax and a wire is inserted into the wax base. See Fig. 10-5.

The wax and part way up the wire is coated with silver conductor. When it is dry, copper plate in an acid bath and then silver or gold plate. When finished, the wax can be boiled out in hot water through a hole cut through the base of the electroformed shell or left in or removed and replaced with a sealing wax or lead.

A female cavity can be plated to electroform a figure. A flexible rubber female mold can be made conductive with Du Pont silver conductor and the object can be electroformed and the mold flexed off and used again and again.

I recommend that you use Du Pont #4817 silver conductor. I have tried many products and have found that #4817 gives the best all-around results over a wide range of uses. It is a pure, very finely divided silver in a high-grade lacquer. You can make any number of items conductive in order to plate them: bugs, leaves, paper, baby shoes, plastic, etc. The cost relative to the area that you can cover is extremely low. You could just about cover your car with a 1-ounce lot.

The old method to make nonconductive surface items conductive is to cover them with finely divided high-grade graphite in a water suspension. This method is rather dirty and calls for quite

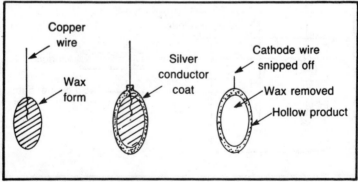

Fig. 10-5. Hollow electro-formed items.

a bit of skill. You can also use copper or bronze powder in a good lacquer. By the time you degrease the bronze or copper powder, mixing it with your lacquer, etc., you are way ahead with the Du Pont #4817.

It is much easier to electroform a part in a negative cavity as opposed to a positive form or mandrel. See Fig. 10-6. One problem with forming on a male mandrel is the removal of the formed part. This can become quite difficult unless the mandrel is expendable, such as a wax form or a low-melting alloy. In the case of an expendable mandrel form—when the form is heated to melt it out of the electroformed part—if it expands faster or to a greater extent than the electroformed part, the part will hot tear or rupture. See Fig. 10-7.

In the case of the female expendable form or cavity, the form expands outward and in fact releases itself from the electroformed part in doing so. See Fig. 10-8.

Now let's talk about treatments to molds (cavities and mandrels), to prevent the electroform being produced from adhering to the cavity or mandrel, and at the same time be electrically conductive. Look at the example of producing silver or gold foil at the beginning of this chapter (Fig. 10-1).

In this case, liver of sulfur is used to produce a sulfided surface on our brass pipe (form). This is referred to as a conductive patina. If you intend to produce a number of the same item (reproductions), you are much better off to use a permanent metal mold cavity. In this case, you have strength and the metal mold

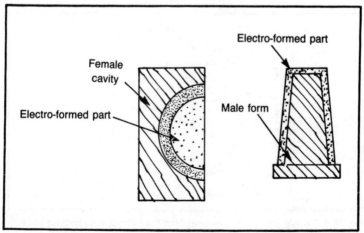

Fig. 10-6. Negative cavity and male mandrel forms used to electro form.

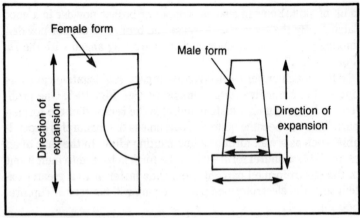

Fig. 10-7. Expansion of female form and male form.

is already electrically conductive. All you need to do is to patina the surface to permit separation of the electroformed item.

DUPLICATIONS FROM A METAL MOLD

Say you have decided that you are going to produce quite a number of silver buttons you have designed or have been commissioned to produce. The number is such that a disposable form would be out of the question. It would require a disposable form for each button electroformed.

The first step is to make a master pattern of what the finished item is to be. You can carve it out of wood, plaster, plastic or wax.

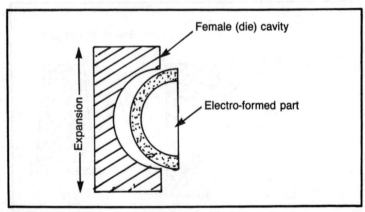

Fig. 10-8. Female cavity expands away from the formed part affecting an easy release.

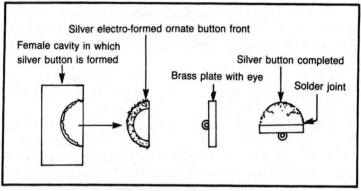

Fig. 10-9. Steps in making an ornate silver front button.

The choice is yours. For example let's tool up to produce 100 or more. In this case, let's say the silver electroformed the face of the button, which is a detailed bar relief. See Fig. 10-9.

You need a female metal cavity in order to produce the silver button fronts via electroforming. Here's how I would tackle it. I would sculpt my master out of jeweler's wax or sculptor's wax. The final electroformed button front is to be 1 inch in diameter. In this case, I will make my master 6 inches in diameter. See Fig. 10-10.

The reason I make the master so large is that it is impossible to get the detail or work with so small an item on the way to a production cavity. Also you would lose much detail in going from a 1 to 1 ratio master to cavity.

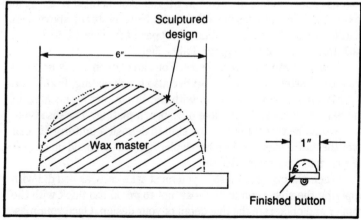

Fig. 10-10. Master pattern size compared with finished product size.

All vertical surfaces of the master must be drafted with no undercuts or back drafted in any way. This would prevent the release of the electroformed part, keying or locking it into the production cavity. See Fig. 10-11.

A very good companion book that can be of assistance in designing patterns for electroforming molds, male or female, is TAB book No. 1510, *Constructing and Using Wood Patterns*.

Now that you have finished the wax master pattern (see Fig. 10-12), you are ready to give the surface of the master a copper plate. The master is coated very carefully with a good conductor coat such as Du Pont's silver conductor #4817 thinned out with butyl acetate. This is done carefully with a fine sable-hair or camel-hair brush. Take care not to obliterate any fine detail of surface texture. Be sure that you implant a stout copper wire loop into the side of your wax master and come up a ways onto the wire with silver conductor. This loop is to conduct the plating current to the silver conductor film. See Fig. 10-13.

THE WAX MASTER

Now you are ready to copperplate the wax master. The reason for the copperplating is to prevent destroying the details in any way when you use this master in the next step.

Now remember that silver (the conductor coat) is soluble in cyanide. You must not copperplate the master in a cyanide copper bath, but you must use an acid bath.

For the copper bath use #1 Copper Bath from Chapter 9: 1 3/4 pounds copper sulfate dissolved in 1/2 gallon of distilled water. Add to this 3 1/2 fluid ounces of sulfuric acid. Now dilute the above with distilled water to make 1 gallon of copper bath. Use 1.5 to 2 volts bath (temperature 90 degrees Fahrenheit).

At this point you have a choice. You can plate in a tank or brush plate the master. See Fig. 10-14. See also brush plating, Fig. 12-14.

My choice would be to go with the brush plating because of the degree of control you have over brush plating. The disadvantage would be that it takes some skill to deposit a uniform deposit over the entire master. With brush plating, you can build up thicker in any area you might desire.

When plating your master, you must take care, as you did with applying the silver conductor coat, not to go on too thick with the copper and obliterate the fine detail of your design. Once your master has sufficient copperplating on it, 5 to 10 thousandths of an inch

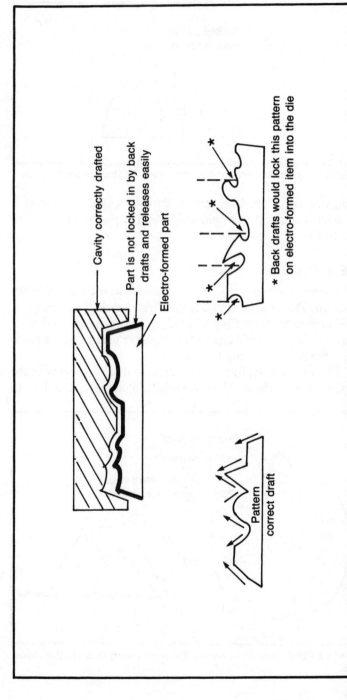

Cavity correctly drafted

Part is not locked in by back drafts and releases easily

Electro-formed part

* Back drafts would lock this pattern on electro-formed item into the die

Pattern correct draft

Fig. 10-11. All vertical surfaces must be drafted to assure release of the electroformed part from the die or cavity.

165

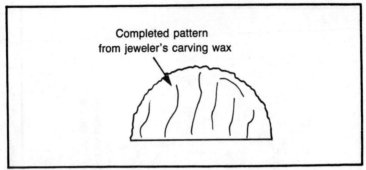

Fig. 10-12. Wax master pattern complete ready for silver conductor coat.

thick, you can, if you like, remove the wax master by melting it out in hot water and replacing it with lead or plaster of paris. See Fig. 10-15.

THE METAL CAVITY

The next move is off to a machine shop to have the metal cavity produced. This is done in two steps. First, a male die or punch of EDM carbon on copper is produced by machining the carbon or copper to the shape and design of our master pattern with a panograph duplicating milling machine.

This not only duplicates the master in detail but reduces the duplicated male die to the desired size. In our case, 1 inch from

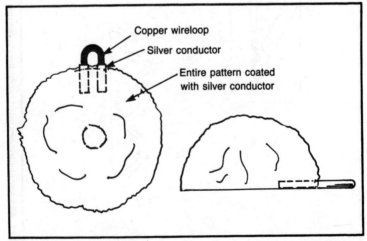

Fig. 10-13. Pattern now with silver conductor coat ready for protective copper plate.

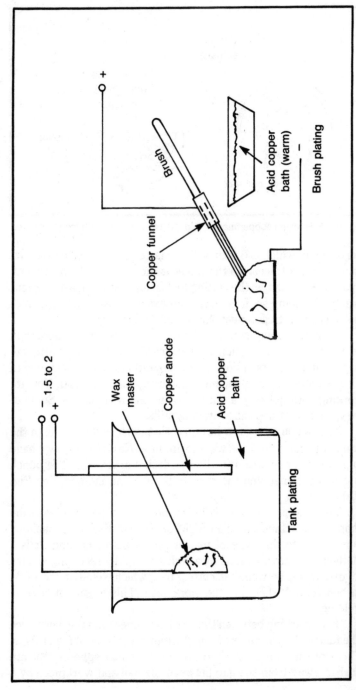

Fig. 10-14. Applying protective copperplating to the wax pattern via tankplating or brushplating.

167

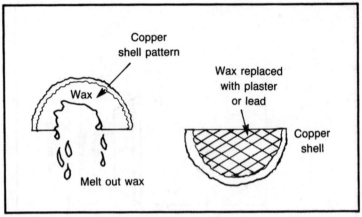

Copper
shell pattern

Wax

Melt out wax

Wax replaced
with plaster
or lead

Copper
shell

Fig. 10-15. Backing copper master (Fig. 10-14) produced with lead or plaster.

the original, which is 6 inches. The master is mounted on the machine under a tracer. As the tracer is moved over the pattern by a panograph linkage, the cutting tool is duplicating this movement exactly. In doing so, it is cutting an exact but reduced version of the master on to a copper die or carbon die. See Fig. 10-16.

Most art supply stores sell an inexpensive pencil panograph device, a close examination of a panograph and its linkage arrangement will clarify its action. The panograph milling machine is of course a much more substantial and complicated animal. You are working with not only a flat plane but one with angles. Some of these machines are called tracing mills.

At this point you now have a male punch or die that is to the size of the button top you want to produce. Now from this we have to produce a metal cavity with our design in reverse. The punch is called a cameo and the reverse is called an intaglio. See Fig. 10-17.

The final production cavity is produced by the machine or die shop by a machine called an EDM or electric discharge machine. Some refer to this type of machine as spark machining. It is a method of removing metal by a series of rapidly recurring electrical discharges between the cutting tool, which would be the EDM carbon (Fig. 10-17), and the workpiece. This is sort of reverse welding.

This sparking between the tool (our cameo) and the workpiece (the female die you are producing) removes particles of metal chips. These are usually in the form of hollow metal spheres that are flushed away from the gap between the tool and workpiece by a

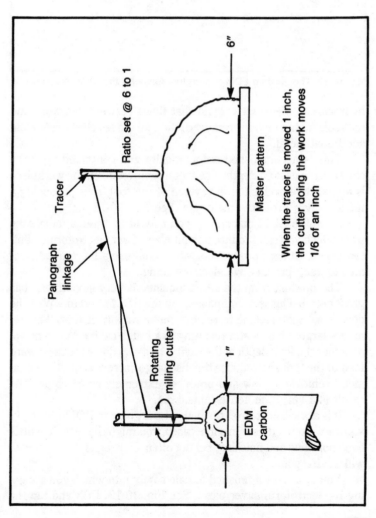

Fig. 10-16. The EDM tool is produced from the master by a panagraph milling machine.

Ratio set @ 6 to 1

Tracer

Panagraph linkage

Rotating milling cutter

Master pattern

6"

When the tracer is moved 1 inch, the cutter doing the work moves 1/6 of an inch

1"

EDM carbon

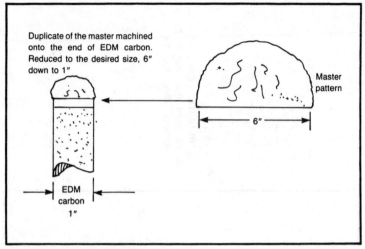

Fig. 10-17. The finished EDM carbon tool ready for the EDM machine.

hydrocarbon die-electric liquid that flows between the work and the tool. As the metal is removed, the tool moves closer removing additional metal.

This is accomplished automatically and continued until the cavity is the desired depth. The metal removed from the workpiece is an exact reproduction in reverse of the tool, thus producing a female cavity from the male tool. See Fig. 10-18.

From the EDM machining, you now have a metal/female die from which you can produce any number of our electroformed button fronts. In high production, you would use a large number of dies to gang produce via electroforming.

The product from the EDM machine is very smooth and has great detail. This is accomplished by the EDM operator. What he does is set the machine to remove metal rapidly at first. This removes larger chips faster resulting in a rough cavity. When he approaches the final depth of the cavity, he slows down the downward feed of the tool and reduces the discharge current so that the final metal removal is slow and produces extremely small chips. The result is a very fine dense female die.

It is always best to let the man who is going to EDM the cavity know its intended use. In some cases, you might have to do a little hand polishing and finishing, but not often. Here again the machinist will advise you.

You now have a finished female cavity into which you are going to electroform silver parts. See Fig. 10-19. Drill and tap the

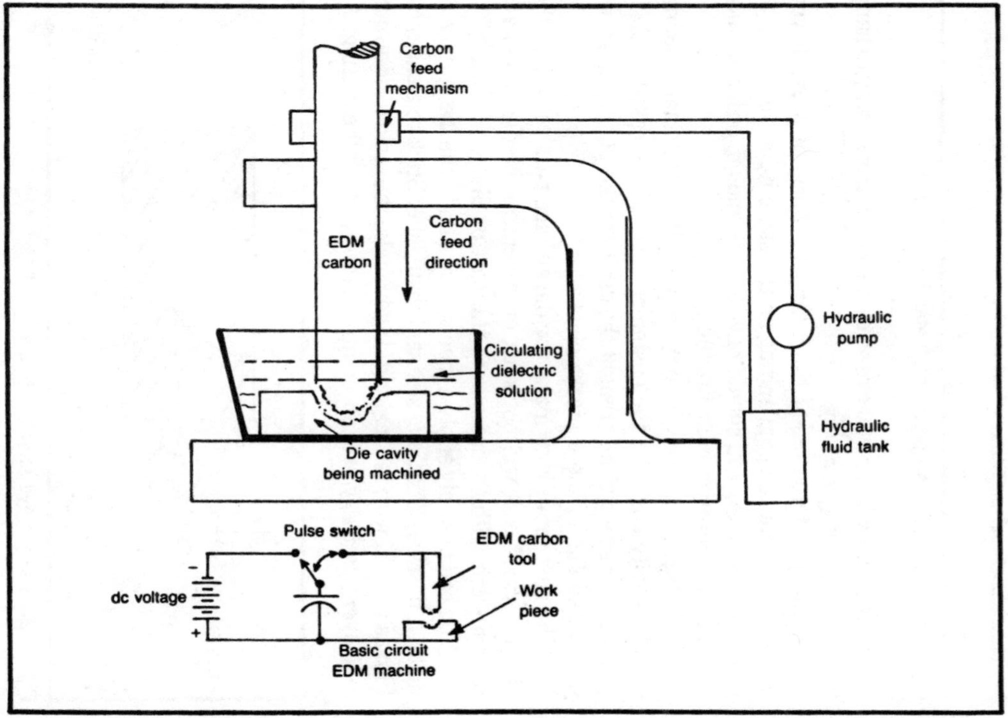

Fig. 10-18. Basic EDM machine.

Carbon feed mechanism

Carbon feed direction

EDM carbon

Hydraulic pump

Hydraulic fluid tank

Circulating dielectric solution

Die cavity being machined

EDM carbon tool

Work piece

Pulse switch

Basic circuit EDM machine

dc voltage

171

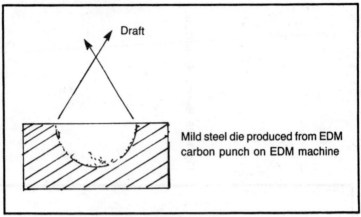

Draft

Mild steel die produced from EDM carbon punch on EDM machine

Fig. 10-19. Finished EDM produced metal die.

cavity and screw in a metal eye so that you will have a way to hang it into the plating. See Fig. 10-20.

At this point you might think this is a world of work. If you intend to reproduce again and again the same item, you must go this way. Of course you should have a large enough order or sales potential to amortize your production die costs.

I have seen the case where the run would be too small to amortize the cavity cost, but the customer covered the cavity cost. It was his property and he brought the cavity to the plater each time he wanted one or more pieces electroformed.

The next move is to make the die surface passive so that the electroformed part will not stick or adhere to the die. You have to remove it without damage to the part or die.

You can possibly apply a mechanical film to the die surface to make it passive. That is easier said than done. Stick to a chemical film as you did with foil making. If you make the mold (cavity) surface over passive, you can run into a problem with the plating. As

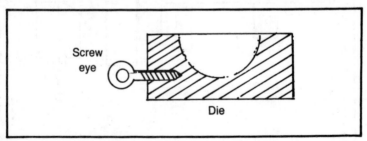

Screw eye

Die

Fig. 10-20. Hanger eye attached to die.

172

it is deposited in the cavity, the plating will fall off as little flakes of metal. This is usually not the case. If the mold surface is too smooth (having little of no tooth to its surface), you can run into this problem.

The principle to this passivity of the surface is to form on the surface of the cavity a film of chemical compound. The film is somewhat conductive due to its thinness. Silver sulfide is quite conductive in a thin film. Of course, most metals will form a thin film over themselves in the form of the oxide of the metal from the oxygen present in the air, aluminum oxide on aluminum, copper oxide on copper, iron oxide (rust) on iron, etc.

Let's assume that for the button mold you had the mold made of plain carbon steel. To make the surface passive, you want to simply oxidize a very thin surface of the mold. You can do this several ways. The simplest way is to make the mold the anode in a dilute warm solution of sodium hydroxide with a carbon or lead cathode. See Fig. 10-21.

In a few minutes, a thin film of oxide will be formed on the die cavity. Remove it and wash in hot running water and then cold running water. Because you don't wish the die to plate all over, but just in the cavity, you must paint the surfaces. Don't plate with asphaltum or any good stop-off varnish. See Fig. 10-22.

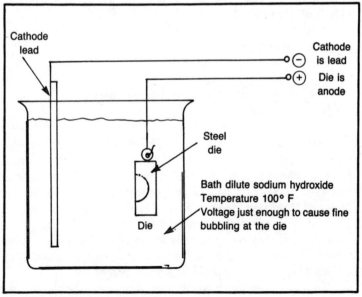

Fig. 10-21. Making the die passive.

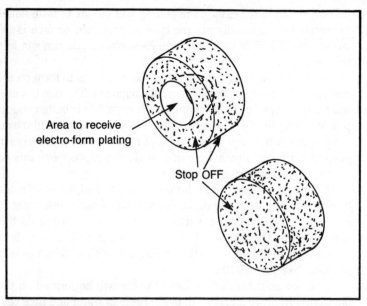

Fig. 10-22. Paint areas of die you do not want to accept plating when electroforming with a stop-off varnish.

Now we are ready for production. The easy part. The cavity is made the cathode. The bath in our case will be #1 Silver Cyanide Bath given in Chapter 9:

8 ounces sodium cyanide.
3 ounces silver cyanide.
1 gallon distilled water.
Voltage is 1 to 2 volts at 70 degrees Fahrenheit.
See Fig. 10-23.

Simply plate until you have the desired thickness for your electroformed piece. Remove the mold and remove the part. A mold for electroforming can be made of wax, wood, plaster or other materials. If plaster, wood, or any porous material is used, it must be sealed to prevent the absorption of plating solution or whatever.

In the case of wood or plaster, they must be soaked in hot paraffin wax until they are completely saturated with wax. Excess wax is wiped from the surface and then further rubbed down with a nylon stocking until the surface is smooth and shiny.

The cavity into which you want to electroform the part is given a thin coat of Du Pont's silver conductor #4817, and then plated with copper from an acid copper bath. This copper surface is given a silver plate.

The silver in the cavity is made passive by brushing it with any soluble sulfide dissolved in a little distilled water. This will give you a black silver sulfide coat over your silver. Silver is a good conductor and will release from the electroformed part. See Fig. 10-24.

Sodium sulfide Na_2S or polysulfide Na_2X_x will react with most metals to form the corresponding sulfides. For example, iron sulfide, lead sulfide, bismuth sulfide, silver sulfide and copper sulfide gives you a good release from cavity or mandrel.

Another very good, simple method is to copperplate the cavity, rinse, and then paint the clean copper surface with any one of your silver cyanide solutions. This will coat the copper with a thin coat of silver (ion exchange) copper displacement. Rinse this with hot then cold water. Now pour 1 fluid ounce of drug-store tincture of iodine in 1 gallon of distilled water. Now you have a 20-year supply. Of course, you could cut this down to a pint if you like.

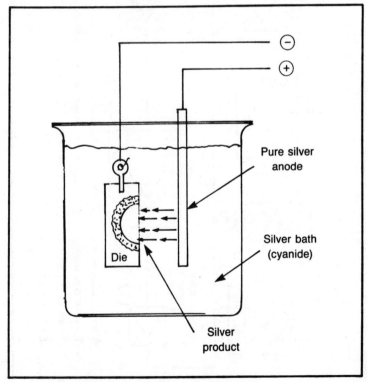

Fig. 10-23. Electroforming a silver button front or top.

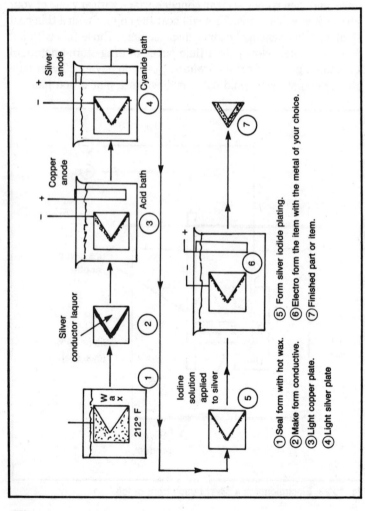

Fig. 10-24. Steps in electro-forming using a porous, non conducting form of wood or plaster.

① Seal form with hot wax.
② Make form conductive.
③ Light copper plate.
④ Light silver plate
⑤ Form silver iodide plating.
⑥ Electro form the item with the metal of your choice.
⑦ Finished part or item.

Silver anode
Cyanide bath ④

Copper anode
Acid bath ③

Silver conductor laquor ②

Wax
212° F ①

Iodine solution applied to silver ⑤

⑥

⑦

176

Now apply (with a fine brush) this iodine solution to the silver coat you applied to the copper. This will produce a thin film of silver iodide (AgI), which will allow you to electroform your item and be able to separate the deposited metal.

Chapter 11

Plating Nonconductors

There is a good market for plating objects that are nonconductors: everything from baby's first shoes to you name it. Although I have had very good results with plating leaves and what have you by coating them with Du Pont silver conductor, and giving them a light deposit of copper in an acid copper bath, you can in some instances have a flaw in the silver coating that will allow the sulfuric acid in the bath to come in contact with the raw item and destroy or damage it.

If the object is of such a nature that it is impossible or impractical to protect it completely, your best approach would be—for very fine objects such as lace, a butterfly, cloth or flowers—to wet the object by dipping and or brushing with a solution of 100 grains of silver nitrate dissolved in 5 ounces of distilled water and 5 ounces of alcohol. If the object can be wetted with this solution, you are home free.

If the object cannot or refuses to wet due to its nature (some leaves and bugs are more or less waterproof), give the item a coat of white shellac that has been thinned out with denatured alcohol. You don't want the shellac so thick as to fill in and obscure the detail on your object. When the shellac is dry, dip or coat the item with a solution of 1/2-ounce silver nitrate, 4 ounces distilled water, and 6 ounces alcohol. Regardless if you went with either process (wet or with shellac and wet), you must now convert the thin film of silver nitrate on the surface into silver sulfide, which is a fairly good conductor of electricity. This we must do with hydrogen sulfide gas. In the bottom of a wide-mouth, gallon-glass jar with a metal screw-top lid, place a few lumps of potassium sulfite or iron pyrite.

Oh yes, solder a hook to the center of the inside face of the lid. Now hang your freshly dipped object from a thread attached to the hook. Cover the sulfide or iron pyrite with a solution of 1 part of sulfuric acid, 8 parts water. Now clap the lid on quickly. This leaves your item covered with a film of silver nitrate hanging in the hydrogen sulfide fumes. This quickly converts the nitrate to a sulfide. When the action quits—which will only take a few minutes—remove the item and go directly into an acid copper bath to plate. Don't breathe the hydrogen sulfide fumes. See Fig. 11-1.

I have seen some very fine, delicate gold jewelry produced by gold electroforming (plating) over a copper male form, and then dissolving the copper with sulfuric acid leaving the delicate gold form. This can also be done in reverse with a female copper form:

Copper is soluble in sulfuric or nitric acid.

Silver is soluble in nitric acid.

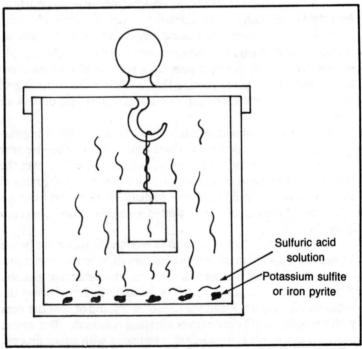

Sulfuric acid
solution

Potassium sulfite
or iron pyrite

Fig. 11-1. Hydrogen sulfide fume jar to make nonconductive objects conductive so they can be electroplated.

Gold is only soluble in aqua regia (royal water).
3 parts hydrochloric acid; 2 parts nitric acid.

You are only limited by your imagination. Think, practice, experiment, and in no time you will be producing beautiful work for fun and lots of profit—if that's your direction.

Chapter 12

Immersion Plating

This plating is often called electroless plating. However, this is a misnomer because an electrical current is involved. The difference is that the current is produced by the reaction of the part being plated and a metal having a higher potential (more positive) will displace a metal of a lower potential in a solution of a salt of the latter metal.

DEPOSIT BY IMMERSION

Example. If you dip a clean piece of copper in a solution of silver salt, a part of the copper enters the solution, displacing the silver that is deposited on the copper. See Fig. 12-1.

The rule is that when one metal is deposited, by immersion, another must go into the solution to take its place. Thus the potential of the metal in solution must be lower than of the metal to be plated. What is happening is that the immersion solution is acting like a dry battery. The table that follows gives you the order of electrical potential: 1 being most positive and 9 being most negative.

1. Zinc
2. Cadmium
3. Lead
4. Tin
5. Iron
6. Copper

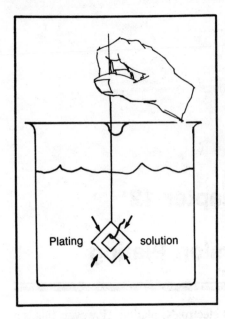

Fig. 12-1. Immersion plating requires no voltage source.

7. Silver
8. Gold
9. Platinum

Any two dissimilar metals when placed in contact produce a current. The amount of current depends upon the amount of potential difference between the two metals. Immersion platings are not very thick and will not stand heavy polishing. Therefore, they are used for cosmetic purposes on items that are not subjected to excessive wear.

Silvering Solution

A
4 ounces caustic soda.
1/2 gallon distilled water.
1/4 ounces silver chloride.
B
2 ounces sodium cyanide.
1/2 gallon distilled water.

Solutions A and B are mixed together and heated to the boiling point in a glass beaker.

A cyanideless solution for silvering is:

12 ounces (salt) sodium chloride.
12 ounces cream of tartar.
1/4 ounce silver chloride.
1 gallon distilled water.

Use a hot but not boiling solution. Add silver chloride when needed to keep it plating.

Gold Immersion

30 grains gold chloride.
4 ounces potassium ferrocyanide.
2 ounces sodium carbonate.
1 quart distilled water.
Use at 170 to 180 degrees Fahrenheit.

Copper

At room temperature for iron and steel.

2 ounces copper sulfate.
1 gallon distilled water.
2 ounces sulfuric acid.

This gives a nice bright copper plate. As soon as the piece is covered remove and rinse in cold water.

To copper zinc items by immersion is not as easy to do but it can be done. Dissolve 4 ounces of copper sulfate in 1 gallon of distilled water. Then add four ounces of ammonia, and wash the zinc item in a dilute solution of hydrochloric acid.

Brassing on Iron and Steel

2 ounces copper sulfate.
2 ounces tin chloride.
1 gallon distilled water.

Nickel

On copper and copper base metals, place 5 ounces nickel oxide in a beaker and bring to a red heat. When cool, add at once to a solution of 4 ounces cream of tartar, 4 ounces granulated tin, and 1 gallon of distilled water. This solution is used boiling. To revive, add nickel oxide (treated as above) in 1-ounce portions.

A widely used electroless process is called the zinc contact method. In this process, the items will continue to plate, and a much heavier deposit can be produced. The parts to be plated are placed in a basket made of zinc. The items to be plated are done by contact with the zinc. The zinc slowly passes into solution, producing the necessary electrical potential to give you the ion exchange.

The outside of the basket is coated with stop-off varnish or asphaltum to increase its life. See Fig. 12-2. Solutions suitable for zinc contact work are as follows.

Silver

9 ounces ammonia.
1 1/4 ounces silver chloride.
Dilute with an equal volume of distilled water.
Add 5 ounces potassium cyanide.
5 ounces sodium carbonate.
2 ounces sodium chloride.
Then add sufficient distilled water to give a volume of 1 gallon. Use at room temperature.

Gold

27 grains gold chloride.
1/2 ounce potassium ferrocyanide.

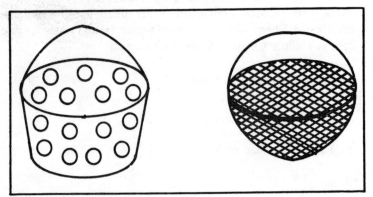

Fig. 12-2. Zinc contact electroless plating.

1/2 ounce caustic soda (lye).
1/2 ounce (salt) sodium chloride.
1 pint distilled water.
Use at 170 to 180 degrees Fahrenheit.

Copper for Iron and Steel

18 ounces cream of tartar.
6 1/2 ounces caustic soda.
5 ounces copper sulfate.
1 gallon distilled water.
Use hot.

Tin for Copper and Brass

2 1/2 ounces alum.
1/2 ounce tin chloride.
1 gallon distilled water.
Use hot.

Nickel for Copper and Brass

5 1/2 ounces nickel ammonium sulfate.
1 gallon distilled water.
Use hot.

Zinc on Iron and Steel

10 ounces zinc chloride.
3 ounces ammonium chloride.
1 gallon distilled water.

I could go on and on with various solutions and variations of solutions. In place of a zinc basket, the parts can be mixed with small pieces of zinc and tumbled in the solution in a perforated plastic drum. Small items such as brass pins, buttons, etc., are tin plated to a bright tin plate by rotating them (mixed with small pieces of zinc) in a solution of 3.5 ounces tin (stannous chloride) 1.3 ounces cream of tartar. See Fig. 12-3.

Brush plating is simple. The solutions used are the same as

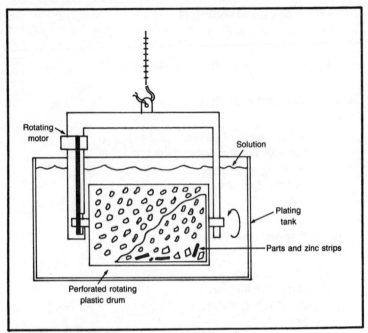

Fig. 12-3. Rotating small items in a plastic drum to tin plate.

you would use when doing standard tank electroplating. Take a good grade of 1-inch-wide paint brush and remove the metal ferrule and replace it with the metal you wish to plate (copper, gold, etc.). For example, let's make a copper brush. We extend the copper ferrule further down the bristles, just letting about 1 inch of bristles extending. This copper ferrule becomes the copper anode. Attach a wire to the ferrule and then to the + of the power source. The – lead from the power source is connected to the object you want to plate. The brush is dipped into the copperplating solution. With the current on, simply paint the plating on. See Fig. 12-4.

Various silvering creams are sold to be used to resilver worn spots on tea sets, etc. These work and are extremely simple to produce.

The simplest one, which works excellently, consists of 1/2 ounce silver chloride and 1 1/2 ounces sodium chloride. Grind these up in a ceramic mortar to a fine powder. Mix well with 1 ounce of cream of tartar. Keep this in a dark bottle that is well capped. To use, simply mix a portion of the above with a small amount of water to a creamy consistency and use a soft, clean cloth to rub this on the spot to be silverplated.

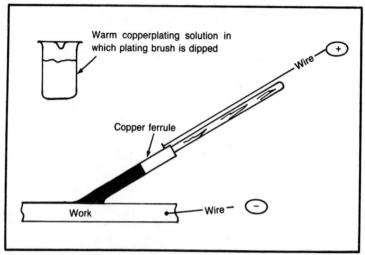

Fig. 12-4. Brush plating set up for copperplating.

VACUUM PLATING

If a metal is raised to its vaporizing temperature, it becomes a vapor just as water when heated becomes a vapor. In vacuum-plating, small staples of the metal you are plating with are hung over a tungsten element in a chamber that also contains the parts to be plated. The air in the chamber is then pumped out to form a vacuum. The tungsten element is then heated by energizing it with an electric current. The staples first melt onto the element. When the metal reaches its vaporizing temperature, the entire chamber becomes filled with the metal vapor that condenses on anything it hits that is below its vapor temperature. Thus the item is coated with a coat of metal.

This is the process by which camera lenses are plated (coated) with various metals. It is a very fast system, with lots of variations, that is widely used to plate cheap plastic novelties and auto trim for cosmetic reasons.

Appendices

Appendices

Appendix A

Suppliers

BASF Wyandotte Corp.
(313) 282-3300
1532 Biddle
Wyandotte, MI 48192

Belke Mfg. Co.
(312) 626-4606
947 N. Cicero Ave.
Chicago, IL 60651

Burt Bricker Inc.
P.O. Box 171
Wilmington, DE 19899

Englehard Minerals & Chemicals Corp.
(201) 589-5000
2655 Route 22
Union, NJ 07083

Paul H. Guesswein Inc.
235 A Park Ave. S.
New York, NY 10003

MacDermid Inc.
(203) 754-6161
50 Brookside Road
Waterbury, CT 06720

SWEST Inc.
(214) 350-4011
10803 Composite Drive
Dallas, TX 75220

Warner Electric Co., Inc.
1512 West Jarvis Ave.
Chicago, IL 60626

Appendix B

Rules

Always add acid to water and slowly and in small amounts. Allow the solution to cool between additions. If too much acid is added to water at one time, the resulting solution can get hot enough to crack the container, boil over, or both. Do all your mixing in a sink. In case of an accident or spill, the solution can be contained and flushed away. Keep a large, open box of soda close by to use to neutralize any acid that might get on your skin. Wear goggles and rubber gloves when making up solutions and plating. Be sure you are working in a well-ventilated area.

With any type of endeavor, whether it is chemical or mechanical, you must adhere to good safety rules and housekeeping. Use hot and cold rinses between operations and solutions. This will not only increase your safety but the work will be of a higher quality. Take your time step by step and you will be amazed with the results.

Gold more or less plates in a straight line. Work plated must be rotated to plate the back or an anode must be present on both sides of the item during plating. See Fig. B-1.

If the work is extremely, deeply recessed, you will have to enter the recessed area with an anode in order to get it plated. See Fig. B-2.

The usual rule of thumb is that the work in order to be properly plated must have an anode whose surface area is four times the area being plated—using an anode for each vertical plane being plated—and shall be no closer than 3 1/2 inches from the object nor further away than 6 inches.

Temperature. You should never plate in a bath below 70

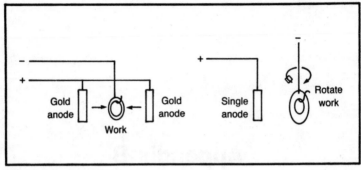

Fig. B-1. Plating gold.

degrees Fahrenheit. An increase in temperature of a plating bath decreases the resistance of the solution to the passage of the current. You can usually get a better plate with less chance of burning when you use less voltage with a heated bath. Even the baths designed for room temperature usually work better when heated.

You will lose some of the water in your solution due to evaporation. Contrary to what some believe, the solution upon losing some of its water will become more concentrated and plate better. Maintain your correct bath volume (thus balance) by replacing the loss of water due to evaporation (not what you spill or lose due to drag out).

Agitation. The bath between the anode and cathode is usually lower in metal content than the bath in other parts of the tank and will result in slowing up the plating process. This problem is easily eliminated by jiggling the work in the bath (stirring). A wooden paddle or spoon used to stir the solution every so often results in better plating. Commercial operations usually have mechanical devices that agitate the work, solution, or both.

Current Effect. With a bath of a given temperature, a weak current will produce a finer-grained, closely knit deposit where a

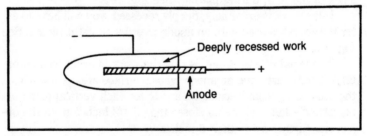

Fig. B-2. Plating a deeply recessed area.

strong current if, too excessive, will result in dark or burned deposits.

Some work, due to its design, presents variable distances from the anode. Work that has deep recesses and a very pronounced uneven surface is an example. The current will take the shortest distance and plate the high points first. Then the metal content in this path becomes exhausted and the current will change its path to one of better conductivity (less resistance) and plate the recesses or points further away. See Fig. B-3. In this case you should not agitate the work or bath because you will prevent the recessed areas from plating correctly or at all. The best method to plate a recessed object would be to have an anode that would be so contoured that all distances would be exactly the same.

The throwing power of a solution (bath) is its ability to plate evenly and quickly even with a recessed surface. Some baths are excellent and some do this poorly. Silver will even plate the back of an object away from the anode. That is great throwing power.

There are variations of plating (other processes) other than the standard electro tank plating, and they bear investigating by the plater. For example, you can produce a gold-gilding powder. This powder, when applied to copper or brass, will give the article a gold plate. It is applied with a cork that has been charred on the end. The process is quite simple. The charred end of the cork is moistened in a strong solution of saltwater (sodium chloride and water). The moistened cork is dipped in the gilding powder and rubbed on the surface of the item to be plated.

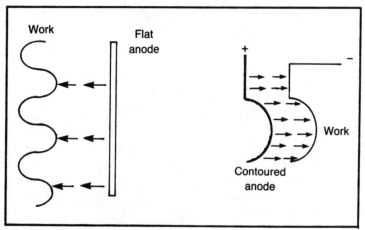

Fig. B-3. Flat and contoured anodes.

The powder is simple to make. Dissolve 45 grains of gold chloride and 15 grains of sodium nitrate in a little distilled water. Now soak some small linen squares in the solution and allow them to dry. When dry, place them in a flask or test tube and heat them until they are charred to a black powder. There is your gilding power. Keep it in a dark bottle in a dark place. A little copper nitrate added to your gold chloride solution will give you a gilding powder that will give you a rose-colored-to-red-colored plating, depending upon the amount added. Work in slowly 2 to 6 grains of copper nitrate.

Appendix C

Measuring Ingredients

The formulas in this book do not require precise measurements. You should, however, have a simple triple-beam gram scale and an assortment of graduates for measuring liquids. You can come close enough using kitchen measuring spoons and measuring cups. The following guide will be of assistance in making up formulations.

Conversions

Gallons = ? pounds (8.33 × specific gravity × the number of gallons). Example: You have 6 gallons of a liquid that has a specific gravity of 1.504. How many pounds do you have?

$$8.33 \times 1.504 \times 6 = 75.16 \text{ pounds}$$

The 8.33 pounds equal the weight of 1 gallon of water, and 1.504 equals the specific gravity of nitric acid.

If you had 6 gallons of nitric acid it would weigh 75.16 pounds.

If you had 6 gallons or sulfuric acid, that has a specific gravity of 1.84, when pure you would have 91.96 pounds. Most acid is sold by weight so much per pound of acid.

Pounds to Gallons

Weight in pounds ÷ 8.33 × specific gravity = gallons. Therefore, if you knew the weight in pounds instead of the number of gallons in the first example, you would go this way:

$$7.516 \div 8.33 \times \text{specific gravity}$$
$$75 \div 8.33 \times 1.504 = 6.003 \text{ gallons}$$

Milliliters

If you have 1 liter of water, how many grams of water would you have? One liter equals 1000 milliliters, and pure water has a specific gravity of 1.504. You would have 1000×1.504 or 1504.0 grams of water.

Grams to milliliters = grams ÷ specific gravity.

Milliliters to pounds = milliliters × specific gravity ÷ 453.56 (No. of grams lb.).

Pounds to milliliters = pounds × 453.56 ÷ specific gravity.

Milliliters to ounces = milliliters × specific gravity ÷ 28.35.

Ounces to milliliters = ounces × 28.35 ÷ specific gravity.

Specific Gravity

Relative density. The ratio of the density of a substance under consideration to the density of pure water at the temperature of its maximum density (4 degrees Centigrade) 39.2 degrees. Fahrenheit.

Liquids

Ounces × 29.56 = milliliters.
Pints × 0.47 = liters.
Quarts × 0.95 = liters.
Gallons × 3.78 = liters.
Milliliters × 0.03 = ounces.
Liters × 2.10 = pints.
Liters × 1.05 = quarts.
Liters × 0.26 = gallons.

Dry

Ounces × 28.35 = grams.
Pounds × 0.45 = kilograms.
Grams × 0.035 = ounces.
Kilograms × 2.21 = pounds.

Dry Equivalents

Teaspoon:
1/8 = 0.54 grams.
1/4 = 1.09 grams.
1/2 = 2.19 grams.
3/4 = 3.28 grams.
1 tsp = 4.38 grams.
Tablespoon:
1/8 = 1.77 grams.
1/4 = 3.54 grams.
1/2 = 7.09 grams.
3/4 = 10.63 grams.
1 tbsp = 14.18 grams.

Pounds to Grams Dry

Pounds:
1/8 = 56.7 grams.
1/4 = 113.4 grams.
1/2 = 226.8 grams.
3/4 = 340 grams.
1 pound = 453.56 grams.

Cups to Grams Dry

Cups:
1/8 = 28.4 grams.
1/4 = 57.0 grams.
1/2 = 113.4 grams.
3/4 = 170.0 grams.
1 cup = 226.8 grams.

Liquid Equivalents

Teaspoon:
1/8 = 0.61 milliliters.
1/4 = 1.23 milliliters.
1/2 = 2.5 milliliters.
3/4 = 3.7 milliliters.
1 Tsp. = 4.95 milliliters.
Tablespoon:
1/8 = 1.84 Milliliters.
1/4 = 3.69 milliliters.

1/2 = 7.4 milliliters.
3/4 = 11.1 milliliters.
1 Tbsp. = 14.8 milliliters.
Ounces:
1/8 = 3.7 milliliters.
1/4 = 7.4 milliliters.
1/2 = 14.8 milliliters.
3/4 = 22.2 milliliters.
1 ounce = 29.57 milliliters.
Cups:
1/8 = 29.6 milliliters.
1/4 = 59.14 milliliters.
1/2 = 118.3 milliliters.
3/4 = 177.4 milliliters.
1 cup = 236.6 milliliters.
Liquid:
1 pint = 473.0 milliliters.
1 quart = 946.0 milliliters.
1/2 gallon = 1.89 liters.
3.4 gallon = 2.83 liters.
1 gallon = 3.78 liters.

The amount of material that will cover a 1/4-square-inch area is called a speck (or as my mother used to say a smidgin).

1 teaspoon = 60 drops.
1 tablespoon = 3 teaspoons.
1 liquid oz. = 2 tablespoons.
1/4 cup = 4 tablespoons.
1 cup = 16 tablespoons.

Appendix D

Weights and Measures

Circular

60 seconds	1 minute
90 degrees	1 quadrant
60 minutes..	1 degree
4 quadrants or 360 degrees	1 circle
30 degrees..	1 sign

Units of Measure

Acre = 208.71 feet square = 43,560 square feet = 4,480 square yards = 0.40687.

Hectares = 4,046.87 square meters.

Barrel = 196 pounds (Flour = 42 Gal. Oil (Standard Oil Co.).

Board Foot = one square foot, one inch thick.

Bushel = 4 pecks = 32 quarts = 2,150.42 cubic inches = 1.24446 cubic feet = 35.23928 liters.

Cable (Cable length) = 720 feet = 120 fathoms = 219.457 meters.

Chain = 100 feet = 100 links = 30.48 meters.

Dram (apothecary) = 3 scruples = 60 grains = 3.888 grammes.

Fathom = 6 feet = 1.829 meters.

Foot = 12 inches.

Furlong = 660 feet = 40 rods, perches or poles = ⅛ mile = 201.17 meters.

Gallon = 231 cubic inches = 3.78543 liters = 3,785.43 cubic centimeters.

Gill = ¼ pint.

Grain = 0.0648 grammes = 64.8 milligrammes.

Hogshead = 63 gallons = 2 barrels (31.5 gallons capacity) = 238.48 liters.

Inch = 2.54 centimeters = 25.4 millimeters.

Karat = 200 milligrammes = 0.2 grammes = 3.0865 grains.

Kilogramme = 1,000 grammes = 2.20462 pounds avd.

Kilometer = 1,000 meters = 3,280.83 feet = 0.62137 miles.

Knot (Nautical or geographical miles) = 6,080.2 feet = 1.15155 miles = 1.85325 kilometers = 1 minute of earth's circumference.

League = 15,840 feet = 3 miles = 4.828 kilometers.

Link = one hundreth of measuring chain = 12 inches (Engineer's chain) = 7.92

inches (Surveyor's chain) = 20 centimeters (Metric Chain).

Liter = 1,000 cubic centimeters = 61.023 cubic inches = 0.0353 cubic feet = 2.1134 liquid pints = 0.2642 gallons.

Meter = 39.37 inches = 3.28 feet.

Miles = 5,280 feet = 1,760 yards. A square mile equals 640 acres = 2.59 square kilometers.

Milligram = 0.001 grammes = 0.015432 grains.

Millimeter = 0.001 meters = 0.03937 inches.

Ounce, Apothecary. Same as troy ounce = 480 grains = 31.104 grammes. Avoirdupois = 437.5 grains = 28.35 grammes = 0.9115 ounce troy or apothecary. Troy (for gold and silver) = 480 grains = 20 pennyweight = 31.104 grammes = 1.097 ounces avd.

Peck = 0.25 bushels = 8.81 liters.

Pennyweight = 24 grains = 1.555 grammes.

Pint, liquid = 0.125 gallons = 0.4732 liters. Dry = 0.5 quarts = 0.5506 liters.

Pipe or Butt = 126 gallons = 2 hogsheads = 476.96 liters.

Pounds, Avoirdupois = 7,000 grains = 16 ounces (adv.) = 0.4536 kilogrammes.

Troy or Apothecary = 5,760 grains = 12 ounces = 0.3732 kilogrammes.

Quart, liquid = 0.25 gallons = 0.94634 liters. Dry = 0.03125 bushels = 67.2 cubic inches = 1.1 liters.

Rod or Perch or Pole = 16.5 feet = 5.5 yards = 5.0292 meters.

Rood = 0.25 acres = 40 square rods = 1,210 square yards = 1,011.72 square meters.

Scruple = 20 grains = 1.296 grammes.

Section of land = 1 mile square = 640 acres.

Stone = 14 pounds (avd) = 6.35 kilogrammes.

Ton (gross) Displacement of water = 35.88 cubic feet = 1,016 cubic meters. (gross or long) = 2,240 pounds (avd.) = 1.12 short or net tons = 1,016.05 kilogrammes = 1.01605 metric tons. (net or short) = 2,000 pounds (avd.) = 20 hundredweight = 907.185 kilogrammes = 0.907185 metric tons = 0.892857 long tons. (metric) = 2,204.62 pounds (avd.) = 1.10231 net tons = 0.9842 long tons = 1,000 kilogrammes.

Cubic Yard = 27 cubic feet = 46,656 cubic inches = 0.76456 cubic meters. Square yard = 9 square feet = 1,296 square inches = 0.836 square meters. Yard = 3 feet = 36 inches = 0.9144 meters.

Appendix E

Conversion Tables

Volume

Multiply		By	To Obtain
Cubic Centimeters			
Dry Volume	(cm.^{3}or cu.cm.)	0.061023	Cubic Inches
Liquid Volume	(c.c.)	.001000	Liters
Liquid Volume	(c.c.)	0.033814	U.S. Fluid Ounces
Cubic Meters	(m.^{3}or cu. m.)	264.17	Gallons
Cubic Meters		61,023.	Cubic Inches
Cubic Meters	(m.^{3}or cu. m.)	35.315	Cubic Feet
Cubic Meters	(m.^{3}or cu. m.)	1.3079	Cubic Yards
Cubic Meters	(m.^{3}or cu. m.)	1,728.	Cubic Inches
Cubic Feet		28,317.	Cubic Centimeters
Cubic Feet	(ft.^{3}or cu. ft.)	0.028317	Cubic Meters
Cubic Feet	(ft.^{3}or cu. ft.)	28.32	Liters
Cubic Feet	(ft.^{3}or cu. ft.)	0.037037	Cubic Yards
Cubic Feet	(ft.^{3}or cu. ft.)	7.4805	U.S. Gallons
Cubic Feet	(ft.^{3}or cu. ft.)	27.	Cubic Feet
Cubic Yards	(ft.^{3}or cu. ft.)	0.76456	Cubic Meters
Cubic Yards	(yd.^{3}or cu. yds.)	61.02	Cubic Inches
Liters	(yd.^{3}or cu. yds.)	0.03531	Cubic Feet
Liters			

Mass and Weight

Multiply	By	To Obtain
Grams (g.)	0.035274	Ounces Avoirdupois
Grams (g.)	0.0022046	Pounds Avoirdupois
Kilograms (kg.)	2.2046	Pounds Avoirdupois
Ounces Avoirdupois (oz.av.)	28.350	Grams
Ounces Apothecary or Troy (oz.ap.or t.)	31.103	Grams
Pounds Avoirdupois (lb.av.)	16	Ounces Avoirdupois
Pounds Avoirdupois (lb.av.)	453.59	Grams

Pounds Avoirdupois (lb.av.)	0.45359	Kilograms
Pounds Apothecary or Troy (lb.ap.or t.)	12.	Ounces Apothecary or Troy
Pounds Apothecary or Troy (lb.ap.or t.)	373.24	Grams
Metric Tons (t)	1,000.	Kilograms
Metric Tons (t)	2,204.6	Pounds Avoirdupois
Metric Tons (t)	1.1023	Short Tons
Short Tons	2,000.	Pounds Avoirdupois
Short Tons	907.18	Kilograms
Long Tons	2,240.	Pounds Avoirdupois
Long Tons	1,016.0	Kilograms
Assay Tons	29.167	Grams

Pressure

Multiply	By	To Obtain
Kilograms per Square Centimeter	14.22	Pounds per Square Inch
Kilograms per Square Centimeter	1.024	Short Tons per Square Foot
Kilograms per Square Centimeter	0.9678	Atmospheres
Pounds per Square Inch	0.07031	Kilograms per Square Centimeter
Pounds per Square Inch	0.0720	Short Tons per Square Foot
Pounds per Square Inch	0.06804	Atmospheres
Pounds per Square Inch	2.307	Feet of Water at 39.2°F.
Pounds per Square Inch	2.036	Inches of Mercury at 0°C
Pounds per Square Foot	0.4882	Grams per Square Centimeter
Pounds per Square Foot	0.00050	Short Tons per Square Foot

Length

Multiply		By	To Obtain
Millimeters	(mm.)	0.001	Meters
Millimeters	(mm.)	0.039370	Inches
Centimeters	(cm.)	0.01	Meters
Centimeters	(cm.)	0.39370	Inches
Decimeters	(dm.)	0.1	Meters
Decimeters	(dm.)	3.9370	Inches
Meters	(m.)	39.370	Inches
Meters	(m.)	3.2808	Feet
Kilometers	(km.)	1,000.	Meters
Kilometers	(km.)	3,280.8	Feet
Inches	(in.)	25.400	Millimeters
Inches	(in.)	2.5400	Centimeters
Feet	(ft.)	12.	Inches
Feet	(ft.)	30.480	Centimeters
Feet	(ft.)	0.30480	Meters
Yards	(yd.)	91.440	Centimeters
Yards	(yd.)	0.91440	Meters
Statute Miles	(st. mi.)	5,280.	Feet
Statute Miles	(st. mi.)	1,760	Yards

Domestic Weights and Measures

Avoirdupois Weight

Troy Weight

437½ grains	1 ounce	24 grains	1 pennyweight

Avoirdupois Weight

16 ounces	1 pound
25 pounds	1 quarter
4 quarters	1 cwt.
20 cwt.	1 ton
2240 pounds	1 long ton

Troy Weight

20 pwt.	1 ounce
12 ounces	1 pound

Apothecaries' Weight

20 grains	1 scruple
3 scruples	1 dram
8 drams	1 ounce
12 ounces	1 pound

Dry Measure

2 pints	
8 quarts	
4 pecks	
36 bushels	

Liquid Measure

4 gills	1 pint
2 pints	1 quart
4 quarts	1 gallon
31½ gallons	1 barrel
2 barrels	1 hogshead

Linear Measure

12 inches	1 foot
3 feet	1 yard
5½ yards-16½ feet	1 rod
320 rods-5280 feet	1 statute mile
6080.20 feet	1 nautical mile

Cubic or Solid Measure

1728 cu. inches	1 cu. foot
27 cu. feet	1 cu. yard
128 cu. feet	1 cord
40 cu. feet	1 ton of ship cargo

Metric Weights and Measures

Metric weights and measures form a decimal system based upon the meter. For convenience, the liter is used as the unit of capacity and the gram as the unit of weight.

The liter equals one cubic decimeter.

The gram is the weight of one cubic centimeter of water at its greatest density

Parts and multiples of the unit are indicated by the following prefixes·

Milli	(m) meaning	1/1000
Centi	(c) meaning	1/100
Deci	(d) meaning	1/10
Deka	(dk) meaning	10
Hecto	(H) meaning	100
Kilo	(K) meaning	1,000
Myria		10,000

Surface Measure

144 sq. inches	1 sq. ft.
9 sq. feet	1 sq. yard
30¼ sq. yds.	1 sq. rod
160 sq. rods	1 acre
640 acres	1 sq. mile
1 acre	43,560 sq. ft

Comparisons

U. S. Bushel	2150.42 cu. inches
Br. Imp. bushel	2218.2 cu. inches
U. S. gallon	231 cu. inches
7.481 U. S. gallons	1 cu. foot
6.229 Br. Imp. gallons	1 cu. foot
6 U. S. gallons	5 Br. Imp. gallons
1 cord	about 103 bushels
1 meter	39.37 in. (U. S. statute)
1 liter	61.022 cu. in. (U. S. Statute)
1 gram	15.42 grains (U. S. statute)
25.4 mm.	1 inch
30.48 cm.	1 foot
1 meter	3.281 feet
1.6093 kilometer	1 mile
6.4515 sq. cm.	1 sq. inch
1 sq. meter	10.764 sq. ft.

Comparisons

1 sq. meter	1,550 sq. inches
1 cu. meter	264.4 U. S. gallons
1 kilogram	2.2046 pounds
1,000 kilograms	1 metric ton
1 kg. per sq. cm.	14.223 lbs. per sq. inch

Area

Multiply		By	To Obtain
Square Millimeters	(mm.^{2} or sq.mm.)	0.0015500	Square Inches
Square Centimeters	(cm.^{2}or sq.cm.)	0.15500	Square Inches
Square Meters	(M.^{2} or sq. m.)	1,000.	Square Centimeters
Square Meters	(m.^{2}or sq. m.)	10.764	Square Feet
Square Inch	(in.^{2}or sq.in.)	645.16	Square Millimeters
Square Inch	(in.^{2}or sq.in.)	6.4516	Square Centimeters
Square Feet	(ft.^{2}or sq.ft.)	144.	Square Inches
Square Feet	(ft.^{2}or sq.ft.)	929.03	Square Centimeters
Square Feet	(ft.^{2}or sq.ft.)	0.092903	Square Meters
Square Yards	(yd.^{2}or sq.yd.)	0.83613	Square Meters
Acres	(A)	43,560.	Square Feet
Acres	(A)	4,840.	Square Yards
Acres	(A)	4,046.9	Square Meters
Square Miles	(mi.^{2}or sq.mi.)	640.	Acres

Index

Index

Other Bestsellers of Related Interest

PRACTICAL BLACKSMITHING AND METALWORKING
—2nd Edition—Percy W. Blandford
This second edition is a complete guide to all the tricks and techniques of the trade—from the basics on metals, alloys, and the metalworking process to projects you can make! Simple instructions and firstrate, detailed illustrations make it easy for a beginner to learn this craft while some projects and their variations are complex enough to challenge even the experienced blacksmith or metal worker. 368 pages, 213 illustrations. Book No. 2894, $17.95 paperback only

THE FIBERGLASS REPAIR AND CONSTRUCTION HANDBOOK
—2nd Edition—Jack Wiley
This guide takes you from choosing your tools to putting the final touches on simple and complex projects. Absolutely no prior experience is required. Step-by-step instructions cover everything from materials selection to the final lamination process and safety precautions. The author includes practice exercises on how to work with glass, cloth, mat, core materials, and resins before starting you on repairs or the customizing of a boat or car. 272 pages, 303 illustrations. Book No. 2779, $14.95 paperback only

THE COMPLETE HANDBOOK OF SAND CASTING—C.W. Ammen
This practical manual teaches you all the age-old skills of casting metals, and shows you how to turn hunreds of metals and alloys into everything from car cylinder heads to metal sculptures, from gun parts to church bells, from reproductions of old toys to impossible-to-find replacement parts. Now, you can create them all in your own workshop, even if you've never worked with metals before! 238 pages, 191 illustrations. Book No. 1043, $12.95 paperback only

THE COMPLETE BOOK OF HOME WELDING—John Todd
This book highlights new arc welding equipment and single-phase wire feeders that greatly simplify the welding process and make it feasible for even novice do-it-yourselfers. The author provides actual step-by-step welding projects that make even complicated welding projects amazingly easy to perform. You'll be able to construct and repair garden carts, car racks, trailers, spiral staircases, and more. 496 pages, 464 illustrations. Book No. 2717, $21.95 paperback, $29.95 hardcover

HOW TO CAST SMALL METAL AND RUBBER PARTS
—2nd Edition—William A. Cannon

Using this excellent sourcebook, you can easily make defect-free castings at an amazingly low cost. Create obsolete or vintage car parts, hood ornaments, garden tools, kitchen utensils, and automotive parts; replace antique parts; reproduce sculpture, and other art! The book includes all-new information on casting polyurethane rubber parts. There's even a listing of sources for supplies and equipment. 176 pages, 143 illustrations. Book No. 2614, $11.95 paperback only

CASTING ALUMINUM—C.W. Ammen

Cast your own automotive or other replacement parts . . . reproduce antique objects . . . cast all kinds of decorative and useful objects in aluminum for your own use, or to sell! It's far easier than you'd imagine! C.W. Ammen leads you step-by-step through every detail in the aluminum-casting process from assembling (and even making) needed equipment to producing your own perfect cast aluminum pieces for hobby or small business purposes! 244 pages, 200 illustrations. Book No. 1910, $14.95 paperback only

Prices Subject to Change Without Notice.

Look for These and Other TAB Books at Your Local Bookstore

To Order Call Toll Free 1-800-822-8158
(in PA, AK, and Canada call 717-794-2191)

or write to TAB Books, Blue Ridge Summit, PA 17294-0840.

Title	Product No.	Quantity	Price

☐ Check or money order made payable to TAB Books

Charge my ☐ VISA ☐ MasterCard ☐ American Express

Acct. No. _____ Exp. _____

Signature: _____

Name: _____

Address: _____

City: _____

State: _____ Zip: _____

TAB Books catalog free with purchase; otherwise send
$1.00 in check or money order and receive $1.00
credit on your next purchase.

Orders outside U.S. must pay with international money order in U.S. dollars.

TAB Guarantee: If for any reason you are not satisfied with the book(s) you order, simply return it (them) within 15 days and receive a full refund. BC

Subtotal $ _____

Postage and Handling
($3.00 in U.S.,
$5.00 outside U.S.) $ _____

Add applicable state
and local sales tax $ _____

TOTAL $ _____